How Would You Vote?

Readings for Critical Thinking in Science

CENGAGE
Learning™

Australia • Brazil • Japan • Korea • Mexico • Singapore • Spain • United Kingdom • United States

CENGAGE
Learning™

How Would You Vote?
Readings for Critical Thinking in Science

Executive Editors:
Michele Baird

Maureen Staudt

Michael Stranz

Project Development Manager:
Linda deStefano

Senior Marketing Coordinators:
Sara Mercurio

Lindsay Shapiro

Senior Production / Manufacturing Manager:
Donna M. Brown

PreMedia Services Supervisor:
Rebecca A. Walker

Rights & Permissions Specialist:
Kalina Hintz

Cover Image:
Getty Images*

* Unless otherwise noted, all cover images used by Custom Solutions, a part of Cengage Learning, have been supplied courtesy of Getty Images with the exception of the Earthview cover image, which has been supplied by the National Aeronautics and Space Administration (NASA).

For product information and technology assistance, contact us at
Cengage Learning Customer & Sales Support, 1-800-354-9706

For permission to use material from this text or product,
submit all requests online at **cengage.com/permissions**
Further permissions questions can be emailed to
permissionrequest@cengage.com

ISBN-13: 978-0-7593-9551-0

ISBN-10: 0-7593-9551-9

Cengage Learning
5191 Natorp Boulevard
Mason, Ohio 45040
USA

Cengage Learning is a leading provider of customized learning solutions with office locations around the globe, including Singapore, the United Kingdom, Australia, Mexico, Brazil, and Japan. Locate your local office at: **international.cengage.com/region**

Cengage Learning products are represented in Canada by Nelson Education, Ltd.

For your lifelong learning solutions, visit **custom.cengage.com**

Visit our corporate website at **cengage.com**

Printed in the United States of America

Contents

Contents

Who Should Know About Our Genetic Makeup and Why?

Tuija Takala; Heta Aleksandra Gylling

Who Has an Interest in the Knowledge, and on What Grounds?

There are four groups of people who may want, or need, to know about our genetic composition. First, we ourselves can have an interest in being aware of all important aspects of our own health status, including the possibility that we nurture genetic disorders which can lead, later in life, to serious disease or early death. There are various studies on people's attitudes towards genetic testing. The ambiguity people have towards genetic knowledge in general seems to be the common result. When people are asked whether they would like to be tested they tend to say yes, but when it comes to actual testing, they are not, after all, too keen to participate.[1 2] Second, there are a variety of people who are—or can become—genetically linked with us, and who can consequently have an interest in the knowledge. These include our family members and especially the individuals with whom we intend to have children. Third, individuals and groups with whom we have contracts, agreements and economic arrangements may well have an interest in knowing about our genetic makeup. This category embraces at least our employers, employees, banks, insurance companies and business associates. Fourth, society as a whole can have an interest in the composition of our genes, both because our health status can influence the contribution we make and because the public authorities may need the information to plan more efficient health care services. In each group the motives are different, and the cases for disclosing vary considerably in strength.

As regards the question of motivation, the term "should" in the question "Who should know?" can be interpreted in three ways. Prudentially speaking, to say that individuals should act in a specified manner is to say that the actions in question tend to promote the long term self interest of these individuals. From the viewpoint of morality, we should do what is right and avoid doing what is wrong. The rightness and wrongness of actions can be defined in different ways. The main moral theories connect the rightness of actions with the observance of virtues, the fulfilment of moral obligations and the avoidance of harm. When it comes to legal thinking, it is held in most liberal societies that countering harm to others should be the primary, if not the only, justification for the use of coercion and constraint.

Tuija Takala, Heta Aleksandra Gylling, "Who Should Know about Our Genetic Makeup and Why?" in *Journal of Medical Ethics*, v. 26, no. 13, June 2000, p.171. Copyright © 2000 by British Medical Association. All rights reserved. Reproduced by permission.

Should People Know About Their Own Genetic Makeup?

Genetic disorders range from the fatal to the trivial, and from the blatantly obvious to the virtually unseen. People who have fair skin have a greater inherited tendency to develop skin cancer than people whose complexions are darker, but this condition is seldom seen as a threatening genetic disorder. The prudential case in favour of knowing about one's genes can be put in its strongest form by studying a genuinely dangerous and universally frightening, instead of an unrecognised, affliction.

Individuals, for instance, whose tumour suppressor gene p53 has undergone a certain mutation carry a disorder known as the LiFraumeni Syndrome, which predisposes them to a spectrum of cancers. The syndrome burdens the individuals with a fifty per cent risk of developing an invasive form of cancer by the age of thirty—a ninety per cent risk by the time they are seventy. While some of these cancers are, as such, curable, it is the accumulation and repetition to which the mutation predisposes individuals which, in the end, makes it lethal.[3] The prudential question is: should people know about conditions like this for their own sakes? One answer is that the knowledge would be beneficial, as it would enable individuals to draw up their life plans realistically. Another response, however, is that if the information does not help people to improve their present or future physical condition, it is not only unwise but also unkind to make them aware of their true condition. It seems that especially when the condition is incurable people cannot have an automatic prudential obligation to acquire the information.

Let us suppose, however, that the disorder is potentially fatal but curable or preventable if diagnosed at an early stage. Assuming that individuals want to live long and healthy lives, it would seem prudential for them to know about such a dormant condition. But there are two different kinds of case here. If the disorder can be removed, and the ensuing disease prevented, by one simple operation which does not pose serious risks to the patient, then all right-minded people have firm prudential grounds for finding out about the condition of their genes. If, however, the treatment is ineffective, painful or difficult to come by, the grounds are less firm.

An additional aspect is that diseases are seldom the result of genetic disorders alone—there are also environmental, psychological and social factors which can contribute to the emergence of basically hereditary ailments. When the prevalence of the actual illness depends on these other factors, it can be argued that people should know about their genetic weakness because the knowledge enables them to adjust their lifestyles accordingly. On the other hand, however, it can also be argued that if there is little the individuals themselves can do to alter their circumstances, the information would be needlessly distressing. And even if they could alter their lifestyles, it is not clear that the knowledge is a blessing, since people may enjoy their lives as they are and resent the idea of changing their behaviour.

The relevant moral considerations regarding our duty to know about our genetic makeup include our virtues and duties, and the possible harm inflicted on others by the lack of knowledge. From the viewpoint of virtue ethics it can be argued that persons of integrity should not be involved in any kind of self-deception, and that they should not, therefore, deliberately overlook facts about their own health status. Those who emphasise our duties, in their turn, can state that we have an obligation to protect others, and those who confine their attention to the undesired consequences of our choices can argue that we should not inflict harm on others either by acts or by omissions if this can be reasonably avoided. But whom and to what degree should we protect from unpleasantness and harm?

If we plan to have children, there are cases in which we have a clear moral duty to find out about the genetic disorders that we carry. Our future children are entitled to be protected from a disease which causes suffering but which could easily have been cured or prevented prior to their birth or in their early infancy. The case of incurable conditions is more difficult to tackle. Some theorists think it would be wrong to bring into existence an individual who suffers from a genetic ailment, when the alternative would have been to give birth to another individual who is healthy. Others argue that even a life which contains some suffering is better than no life at all, and that the potential individuals who are not given the chance to live are therefore wronged by the decision not to bring them into existence.

Although all main branches of ethics seem to oblige us to know about our genetic makeup, at least in some cases, no legal duties can be derived from these obligations. People cannot really be forced into moral integrity, and the harm inflicted on future children by lack of genetic knowledge cannot really be regulated with any accuracy. Parents can conceivably be blamed and even punished for harming their unborn or newly born children by direct physical violence, but it would be far too complicated to prove that a genetic disorder results from a malicious, negligent and deliberate decision not to know about one's genes.

Should Our Reproductive Partners or Business Associates Know?

The individuals with whom we intend to have children and our business associates both have, in their parental or professional roles, good prudential grounds for finding out about our genetic disorders. Our reproductive partners can legitimately try to ensure that the offspring we produce are healthy and do not have to suffer unnecessarily from hereditary diseases. The individuals with whom we have business relations have a well-founded interest in knowing whether we are able to keep our promises and fulfil our obligations.

The moral case our reproductive partners have for acquiring information concerning our genes is strengthened by the interests of our prospective children to be healthy, but it is also weakened by the fact that individuals have no moral obligation to produce offspring with other specified individuals. Our partners can have a moral obligation to avoid bringing into existence a child whose genetic disposition makes her or his life miserable, especially if the alternative is to have a healthy child. But this obligation can be discharged by choosing another partner, as it is nobody's duty to have children with us. If harm might befall us should our genetic disorders be revealed, our reproductive partners can have no overall moral, let alone legal, right to know about them.

Economic considerations can make it desirable for our employers, employees, business associates and insurance companies to find out what genetic disorders we carry. Since some of our hereditary weaknesses, such as the mutation of gene p53, are potential causes of disabling illness and premature death, contracts and agreements which are made with us without knowing about such conditions can be highly unprofitable. These reasons can be seen as prudential or moral, depending on who will be harmed by our inability to fulfil the contracts. If only our direct business associates are harmed, then the reason is prudential; if the harm is extended to their shareholders, clients and employees, then the grounds for disclosure are moral.

But the obligation to protect others against economic loss is not as strict as the duty not to inflict suffering on innocent individuals. All economic decision making is based on risk assessment, and from the point of view of our business associates the composition of our genes is only one unknown factor among others in the cost-benefit analysis. Many people would, of course, like to ascertain the state of our genes, but if this interest is founded on a desire to maximise economic profits, then almost any reluctance that we may have against parting with the information provides, both morally and legally speaking, a sufficiently good reason not to satisfy their curiosity. Grounds for such reluctance can be found in the distress that the knowledge can cause, and in the fear of discrimination which can accompany the disclosure of our medical status to others.

The representatives of insurance companies can argue that if we do not report our genetic disorders when we apply for life or health policies, other policyholders will be unjustly burdened by the unforeseen cost of our medical treatment and premature death. If this argument is presented in the framework of consequences and harm, then the economic loss possibly inflicted on others is outweighed in a level-headed comparison by our own distress caused by the unwanted knowledge and our fear of discrimination. It can also be argued that life and health policies should not be made more expensive for those who carry mutated genes, because many other factors besides the biological determine whether people actually get ill or not. Genetic disorders cannot always be seen as diseases in their early stages. An obvious injustice related to differential insurance practices is that they punish those who are already genetically worse-off by denying them life and health policies, or by enlarging the payments.[4]

The insurers' appeals to justice can also be founded on the reciprocity of duties and rights favoured by many moral philosophers. It can be held that we should not do to others what we would not like them to do to us, and that when we profit at other people's expense by refusing to disclose our genetic weaknesses we are violating this principle. The problem with this argument is that it is not normally considered unjust to collect a compensation when the terms of the policy are met. Insurance companies define the payments of life and health policies on the basis of epidemiological data, and the expenses caused by known genetic disorders should already have been accounted for, at a general level, in the fees.

The only way to benefit unfairly at the expense of others would be, within the duty-based approach, wilfully to conceal one's genetic condition from the underwriter. This is wrong within ethical views which absolutely condemn lying. The model applies to situations where would-be policyholders are explicitly asked by the insurance company to reveal the genetic disorders they know they have. But this kind of thinking creates more problems than it solves. Since individuals cannot have a legal duty to know about the condition of their genes, the prohibition against active lying generates a duty to tell only for those who have voluntarily acquired the information, and for those who have been informed against their will. As for the latter group, a special legal duty to be truthful would be grossly unfair in view of the fact that members of this group would already have been victimised once if they had been tested without consent.[5] For those who have voluntarily tested themselves, the legal obligation to tell the truth would be equally indecent. It is, after all, in the best interest of society that its members freely acquire information about their health status. The duty of honesty would, however, make it more profitable for individuals to remain in ignorance.

Should Our Health Care Providers Know?

Those who cater for our health care needs have at least two good reasons for wanting to know about the composition of our genes. Physicians can monitor our health-related needs more effectively and offer more reliable treatments if they are fully informed about all the relevant facts. And public health authorities can collect knowledge regarding the genetic makeup of the population, and plan in advance health care services which are likely to meet the future needs of citizens.

The Hippocratic tradition requires physicians to be beneficent, that is, to provide their patients with the best treatment available.[6] Doctors can refer to this tradition and argue that in order to fulfil their duties they should be allowed to know about the genetic disorders of their patients. But the significance of beneficence has been undermined by the introduction of the principle of autonomy to health care ethics. The principle of autonomy states that medical professionals ought to respect the self-determined, self-regarding choices of their informed and competent patients even if the choices in question are potentially harmful.[7 8] According to this maxim, people are entitled to remain in ignorance concerning their genetic disorders, which means that physicians cannot use paternalistic arguments to back their claims that they should be informed about their patients' condition.[9]

The work of public health authorities is often based on epidemiological data which is acquired by gathering information about the health and illness of citizens. If this work promotes human wellbeing and reduces human suffering, then we are, to some degree at least, morally obliged to reveal facts which can help the authorities. Furthermore, if we believe that other people should not hinder public health programmes by withholding personal information, then we too have an initial duty not to withhold information concerning ourselves. When it comes to absolutely binding moral duties and legally enforced obligations, however, the situation is different. The harm inflicted on others by the nondisclosure of genetic data is indirect and uncertain, while the harm inflicted on individuals with genetic disorders in the form of distress and discrimination is direct and tangible. The argument from the reciprocity of obligations is no more convincing. In an ideal world we would, no doubt, like individuals to do their best to help the public authorities in their attempts to provide better health care services. But in an ideal world we would not have to live in fear of discrimination should we reveal our genetic ailments to our potential employers or insurance companies.

Who Should Know?

Who, then, should know about our genetic makeup, and why? If the picture given in this paper is not distorted, we ourselves can have both prudential and moral reasons for knowing about some of our possible genetic disorders. Our reproductive partners, business associates and health care providers have similar reasons for acquiring the information. But when it comes to duties and rights which could be enforced by law, these reasons are not firm enough to support them. As long as people whose genes deviate from those of the average individual are likely to face suspicion and discrimination, societies cannot legitimately force people to know about their hereditary composition.

Acknowledgements

Our thanks are due to Veikko Launis, University of Turku, and to two anonymous referees of the *Journal of Medical Ethics* for helpful comments.

References and Notes

[1] Mitchell J, Scriver CR, Clow CL, Kaplan F. What young people think and do when the option of cystic fibrosis carrier testing is available. *Journal of Medical Genetics* 1993;30:538–42.

[2] Tambor ES, Bernhardt BA, Chase GA, Faden PR, Geller G, Hofman KJ, et al. Offering cystic fibrosis carrier screening to an HMO population: factors associated with utilization. *American Journal of Human Genetics* 1994;55:626–37.

[3] Malkin D, Li FP, Strong LC, Fraumeni JF Jr, Nelson CE, Kim DH, et al. Germ line p53 mutations in a familial syndrome of breast cancer, sarcomas, and other neoplasms. *Science* 1990; 250:1233–8.

[4] Harris J. *The value of life: an introduction to medical ethics.* London: Routledge & Kegan Paul, 1985:87–110.

[5] On the nature and significance of informed consent in genetic testing see, for example, Juengst ET. Genetic diagnostics. In: Fischer EP, Klose S, eds. *The diagnostic challenge, the human genome.* Mannheim: Boehringer Mannheim GmbH, 1995: 207–8.

[6] Beauchamp TL, Childress JF. *Principles of biomedical ethics* [4th ed]. New York and Oxford: Oxford University Press, 1994: ch. 5.

[7] See reference 6:59–105.

[8] Hayry H. *The limits of medical paternalism*. London and New York: Routledge, 1991: ch 7.

[9] See reference 8:154–5.

Tuija Takala, Msc(soc), is a Research Fellow in the Department of Philosophy, University of Turku, Finland. Heta Aleksandra Gylling, BA, MA, MSc(soc), LicSc(soc), DSc(soc), is a Senior Research Fellow at the Academy of Finland and a Docent of Practical Philosophy at the University of Helsinki, Finland.

Pro & Con: Should Preconceptional and Prenatal Cystic Fibrosis Carrier Screening Be a Routine Part of Obstetrical Care

Dr. Michael T. Mennuti; Katie Richardson

Yes

All physicians who do Y E S obstetrics should offer screening to people with a family history of cystic fibrosis, reproductive partners of people who have the disease, and couples in whom one or both members are white and who are planning a pregnancy or seeking prenatal care.

Those recommendations were issued in September 2001 by the American College of Obstetricians and Gynecologists and the American College of Medical Genetics (ACMG), in jointly issued guidelines for cystic fibrosis (CF) carrier screening.

The guidelines were intended to specify what's best for patients—not consider whether physicians have time to do this, whether insurance will pay for it, or whether CF carrier screening will be controversial relative to the abortion issue.

In 1989, investigators cloned the gene for CF and identified its most common mutation. At that time, CF screening had about a 70% sensitivity, meaning that about half of the couples who would have a child with CF would learn that they are at high risk.

During the 1990s, investigators discovered more than 900 different mutations of the CF gene. Meanwhile, pilot trials of CF carrier screening showed two things: Patients generally were not interested in getting screened until they were already pregnant. And when some couples were offered the screening, they decided to have it. If one or both parents were found to be a CF carrier, they would often make decisions to continue or terminate the pregnancy based on information obtained by prenatal diagnosis.

The latter observation led to a recommendation in 1997 by a National Institutes of Health consensus panel: There are enough people who want CF carrier screening that we need to make it available to them.

Some studies have shown that when physicians offer CF carrier screening, patients assume that they have to undergo it. Because of this, the ACOG-ACMG guidelines recommend that the initial information about CF carrier screening should come from someone other than the physician. We want patients to understand that it's their choice.

I believe that physicians have a legal obligation to offer CF carrier screening. I'm not a legal expert, but I would have a hard time being a defense expert in a case of a child born with CF whose parents weren't offered the opportunity to be screened.

ACOG and ACMG have developed materials about CF carrier screening for physicians and patients. No one knows what percentage of patients who are offered the test will want it. In pilot studies, the acceptance rate was mostly in the 70%–80% range, and it sometimes exceeded 90%. But those data come from clinical research settings, and I would expect lower rates in clinical practice.

Dr. Michael T Mennuti is professor of ob.gyn., human genetics, and pediatrics at the University of Pennsylvania, Philadelphia.

No

But if physicians are encouraging this test or suggesting it as part of a routine protocol for deciding whether to continue a pregnancy, that's wrong. The diagnosis doesn't have to mean doom and gloom for parents who are CF carriers. You simply don't know how life may turn out for someone with CF.

If a patient wants to undergo CF carrier screening for curiosity's sake, that's fine. And I realize that physicians may feel that they need to offer such testing to protect themselves legally.

I'm a good example of how a person with CF can live a full, productive life. I was diagnosed with CF when I was 3 years old, but that didn't stop me from having a normal life. I went to school, played sports, and went to college and law school. I'm now almost 35 years old, I work full time as a lawyer, I'm married, and I have two children.

I had a sister and a cousin who died of CF, so when other members of my family began to reach childbearing age, I know they all underwent CF carrier screening.

I don't disagree with the testing per se, but in general, I don't think the intent is to satisfy curiosity. In my opinion, physicians usually offer the test so that they can advise termination of pregnancy if one or both parents are found to be a CF carrier. There really isn't anything physicians can do prenatally for someone with CF.

Before we had our first child, my husband chose not to undergo CF carrier screening. He did not want the results to factor into the equation of whether we had children or not. I left the decision up to him.

Routine CF carrier screening as part of preconceptional and prenatal care is unfair, because physicians generally don't offer adequate counseling about CF before the woman or couple decides whether to terminate the pregnancy.

Most physicians have no idea what life is like for a person with CF. They view CF as a life-threatening disease, period. I'm not denying that CF is a serious disease, but physicians rarely explain that the life expectancy for people with CF is into adulthood and getting longer each year. They rarely note that therapies and medications have progressed tremendously. And they rarely emphasize that someone can be born with CF and live for all intents and purposes a relatively normal life.

CF is not the end of the world. People with CF may need extra medications or may go to the doctor more often. But people born with asthma or diabetes face similar challenges. People with CF are growing up, getting married, and leading productive lives. Some are not so lucky, but that can be the case with anyone. There are no guarantees in life.

Sure, it would be nice to live without CF. But if given the choice, I would rather live with CF than not be alive.

Katie Richardson is a lawyer who practices in Alexandria, Va.

Individual Responsibility for Health: Decision, Not Discovery

Scot D. Yode

While I was in graduate school my family and I frequently ate Sunday lunch out with several other families. On one occasion our group was joined by an elderly couple on leave from an overseas assignment. After lunch the husband excused himself, returning to the table a few minutes later with a large and mouth-watering Cinnabon oozing with butter and frosting. As he sat down to his treat our seven-year-old son, Nathan, eyed him thoughtfully. Then, with concern, and not just a little reproach, he asked the unassuming man, "Do you know how many grams of fat are in that?" When the visitor replied that he did not, Nathan told him the precise number and lectured him on fatty foods and the risk of heart disease. The man listened graciously, then reassuringly noted that since he had only one Cinnabon a year, there was probably no need to worry.

The story shows how information about health and illness permeates our lives. We are preoccupied with understanding the determinants of health and illness, particularly those over which we have some control. News reports inform us daily of new discoveries: obesity is linked to premature death; certain genes predispose one to breast cancer, heart disease, or Alzheimer's disease; red wine can reduce one's risk of heart disease. There are a number of reasons why we thirst for such information. Most obviously, we use it to enhance our ability to cure or prevent illness. We also use it to direct money toward research that promises the greatest results. (1) Finally, but importantly, we use information regarding the determinants of health to assign responsibility for health and illness. Robert Veatch anticipated this trend more than twenty years ago:

> We may not be far from the day when we can say that all health problems can be viewed as someone's fault—if not our own fault for poor sanitary practices and lifestyle choices, then the fault of our parents for avoiding carrier status diagnosis, amniocentesis, and selective abortion; the fault of industries that pollute our environment; or the fault of the National Institutes of Health for failing to make the scientific breakthroughs to understand the causal chain so that we could intervene. (2)

The inclination to find fault takes on special significance when we attribute responsibility to individuals for their own health. We know that many behaviors or "lifestyle choices," including smoking, excessive drinking, not exercising, indulging in a high-fat diet, and failing to wear seatbelts, either cause illness or put health at risk. We are told how to improve our health or reduce our risk of illness by eating properly, exercising regularly, or taking aspirin daily. While this information empowers us, it also burdens us. If we can control our health, we can be blamed for being ill. "The emphasis on healthy lifestyles," physician Faith Fitzgerald writes in the New England Journal of Medicine, "although salutary in many ways, has a very dark side to it and has led to the increasing peril of a tyranny of health in the United States." (3)

Whether there is truly a tyranny of health or not, assessments of personal responsibility for health certainly affect our lives in many ways. Most overtly, we use them to justify formal policies—broadly referred to as "lifestyle proposals"—designed to influence behavior or make people bear the burden for health-related behavior. For instance, governments impose "sin" taxes, (4) seatbelt laws, and regulations governing the distribution of transplantable organs; (5) insurers refuse coverage, impose coverage restrictions, or increase premiums for people who smoke, don't wear seatbelts, or are obese; and employers implement wellness incentives or refuse to hire people who smoke. (6) While they have not reached the level of formal policies, assessments of personal responsibility for health are raised in discussions of allocating scarce health care resources, (7) and they have even emerged in discussions about medical practice. Some physicians, for instance, have asked whether patients should be held accountable for not complying with prescribed medical treatment. (8)

Assessments of personal responsibility for health and illness often affect people in more subtle ways. Health promotion and fitness programs, magazines, videos, websites, and television shows appeal to our self-interest, our self-image, and even our personal sense of responsibility. As a runner I read with some interest a health promotion newsletter that listed the number of minutes one must run or walk in order to burn off the calories ingested in common treats. There was good news and bad. My dislike of Big Macs (66 minutes) is now accompanied by a certain moral smugness, but I'll probably never be able to enjoy another serving of my beloved pecan pie (73 minutes) without a pang of guilt. (9) Finally, there is evidence that we attribute moral qualities to people based on their health. We tend to attribute positive characteristics, such as the ability to self-manage, work hard, delay gratification, and control impulses, to people who have the right weight and shape, and who are physically fit. Conversely, those who have the wrong body shape or are overweight or unfit are thought to be indulgent, lazy, and lacking in self-control. (10)

Because claims of personal responsibility for health affect our lives in so many ways, it is critical that they not be arbitrary or discriminatory. We want to avoid penalizing or stigmatizing people for injuries or illnesses for which they are not responsible. Nor should we arbitrarily select certain health risks out for sanction while ignoring others. The familiar response to this concern is to appeal to scientific and medical research to impartially discover whether an individual is responsible for his or her illness. Discoveries based on sound research, it is hoped, will be free from bias.

I want to argue that this approach is seriously flawed. Although empirical research from the scientific and medical communities is essential, construing responsibility for health or illness as something we merely discover is misleading and potentially dangerous, as it can result in real but hidden bias. Determinations of responsibility for health are as much decision as discovery.

Before I can adequately defend this claim I need to clarify two issues. First, what do I mean by the phrase "responsibility for health"? Second, what do I mean when I say that determinations of responsibility for health are as much decision as discovery?

The Ambiguity of Responsibility

We complicate discussion of personal responsibility for health when we fail to recognize the different ways in which we use the term "responsibility for health." Consider, for example, the relatively simple statement, "Joe is responsible for the cirrhosis of his liver." Discussions of personal responsibility for health frequently proceed as if statements such as this are clear and precise, when in fact they are often ambiguous. A person making this statement might mean one, or some combination, of the following three different things. (11)

First, because we sometimes use "responsibility" to mean "causality," the comment might be a response to the question, "What physically caused the cirrhosis of Joe's liver?" The statement might simply mean that his alcohol consumption, as opposed to some other factor such as hepatitis, brought about Joe's liver disease. On the surface, at least, statements of causality are purely descriptive statements of fact. They are statements about the way the world is and how it operates. Causal responsibility for health can be attributed to a wide variety of things—to human actions, to microorganisms, to genes, to the environment, to substances, to biochemical mechanisms, and so on.

Second, the comment might be a statement of moral responsibility, as opposed to causality. That is, it might be a response to the question, "Who is to blame for the cirrhosis of Joe's liver?" While the concept of moral responsibility includes the notion of being either blameworthy or praiseworthy, most discussions of personal responsibility for health focus on blameworthiness. That is, though we sometimes praise people for their healthy lifestyles, we are usually more concerned with whether or not to blame individuals for behaviors that lead to illness or injury, or that present a risk to health. Unlike causal responsibility, moral responsibility can only be assigned to moral agents. It is Joe, not his action or the alcohol, that is morally responsible.

Finally, our statement may be a claim about what I will refer to as "social liability." (12) Used in this sense, the claim that Joe is responsible for the cirrhosis of his liver might be a response to the question, "Should we implement social policies designed to reduce or make people bear the burdens of their alcohol consumption?" For instance, we might be describing or defending a policy that would give Joe lower priority for liver transplantation than patients whose end-stage liver disease did not result from alcohol abuse.

Most discussions regarding personal responsibility for health, particularly those concerned with lifestyle proposals, focus on the question of social liability. They address the question of when, if ever, we can justify using the power of the state, insurer, or employer to influence or hold people accountable for their health or for behavior that poses a risk to their health. (13) This is an important question, for lifestyle proposals have the potential to impact people's lives significantly. However, I want to focus on moral responsibility and causality rather than social liability, for two reasons.

First, the claim that determinations of social liability are as much decisions as discoveries is not particularly controversial. After all, we create, choose, or select polices, we do not discover them. Because we understand this, we generally at least recognize the need to guard against bias as we formulate policies. This is not so obviously the case for determinations of moral responsibility, and even less so for determinations of causality. In comparison to determinations of social liability, we tend to view these as objective discoveries, and thus as less prone to bias.

Second, all justifications for social liability depend on assessments of causality, and many depend on assessments of moral responsibility. It makes sense to try to influence someone's behavior in the name of health only if the behavior causes or increases the risk of illness or injury. Furthermore, often (though not always) justifications of lifestyle proposals depend on the individual's moral responsibility for his illness, injury, or risky behavior. Thus, if determinations of causality and moral responsibility are as much decisions as discoveries, as I will argue, then they introduce an additional, but often unrecognized source of potential bias into determinations of social liability. One of my goals in writing is to draw attention to these possible sources of bias so that they can be more consciously guarded against.

A Pragmatic View of Discoveries

The second preliminary issue I need to address is the meaning of my claim that determinations of responsibility for health are as much decisions as discoveries. The understandings of causality and moral responsibility I want to defend have their roots in philosophical pragmatism. For this reason, they can perhaps best be understood in contrast to any view that regards causality and moral responsibility as simple brute facts about the world—facts that exist completely independent of who is assigning responsibility and how or why it is being assigned. Viewing facts about causality and moral responsibility as brute descriptive facts implies that they are independent of us, "out there" waiting to be discovered in the way that one might discover how much a stone weighs. The stone weighs a certain amount regardless of who weighs it or why it is being weighed. Likewise, in this view, whether someone caused or is morally responsible for a health condition is a fact independent of us, and can be discovered through adequate scientific and medical research.

A pragmatist would reject the assumption that facts about causality or moral responsibility exist independent of persons, communities, and the social practices they establish to assess responsibility. This claim is not specific to causality or moral responsibility; pragmatists argue that all human knowledge is dependent on us. Behind this conviction is the insight that all knowledge is agent-centered. We do not and cannot seek knowledge as disinterested spectators who impartially observe and describe the world, but rather as agents in the world who strive to solve problems and make sense of the world. This means not only that we cannot speak of the world or make claims about it apart from how we are able to humanly conceptualize, experience, and describe it, but also that human knowledge is dependent on us because it is instrumental. What we know about the world cannot be fully understood independent of how and why we know it—what social practices are used to establish facts and what human values, goals, and interests those facts serve. Facts and values are inextricably entangled. According to the pragmatist, facts independent of us, facts that are merely "out there" waiting to found and are not affected by human interests, do not exist. In the words of William James, "The trail of the human serpent is thus over everything." (14)

The claim that determinations of responsibility for health are as much decision as discovery is an attempt to express these pragmatic convictions. (15) It implies three things. First, the world does not simply impose determinations of causality or moral responsibility on us; determinations are dependent on our values, goals, and social practices. Second, because our values, goals, and social practices can and do change, our determinations are flexible or malleable to a certain degree. They are subject to revision. This is not to say that there may not be a correct determination of causality or moral responsibility in a particular situation. It merely means that what counts as such will depend on the particular context. Finally, if these statements are true, then we cannot rely solely or unquestioningly on scientific and medical research to provide objective assessments of responsibility.

This does not imply that we must give up on objectivity. It is still an important goal. However, a pragmatist must be suspicious of any interpretation of objectivity that claims to provide a neutral or detached perspective, independent of human values, goals, and social practices. (16) To avoid arbitrary or discriminatory assessments, we must also employ deliberative processes in which we openly examine the values, goals, and social practices that influence our determinations of responsibility. The danger of reports that present claims of responsibility for health as discoveries of simple descriptive fact is that they seem to make such examination unnecessary or irrelevant; they allow us to hide potentially arbitrary or discriminatory judgments and policies behind a veil of supposed objectivity. My goal in this paper is not to defend any method of examination, but only to highlight the pragmatic nature of claims of personal responsibility for health that make such processes crucial.

Moral Responsibility

Is there a fact, independent of us, regarding whether a person is morally responsible for the state of his or her health? To answer this question, it is necessary to look a bit more generally at the notion of moral responsibility. (17) Simply stated, we are morally responsible for outcomes or events that can be ascribed to us as agents. This simple statement, however, hides a great deal of complexity and requires further analysis. My approach to this problem is itself pragmatic. Rather than engage in conceptual analysis to clarify the notion of moral responsibility, I want to look at our actual practices of holding people morally responsible. More precisely, because I am focusing on the more negative assessments of responsibility, I want to look at our practices of blaming. The following observations are particularly relevant in the context of personal responsibility for health.

First, we hold people morally responsible for actions that create a risk of harm as well as for those that actually cause harm. In the context of personal responsibility for health this means that we blame people for actual illnesses and for actions or lifestyle choices that carry the risk of injury or illness even if no injury or illness actually occurs. For instance, regardless of whether she actually suffers from a smoking related illness, we might hold a smoker morally blameworthy because smoking carries with it a known and avoidable risk of illness. (18)

Second, we do not hold people morally responsible for all harms or risks of harm, but only for those that can be ascribed to them as agents. This significantly affects the scope of responsibility, broadening it in some respects and narrowing it in others. On the one hand, it broadens the scope of responsibility in that it allows us to blame people both for harm (or risk of harm) that they bring about and for harm (or risk of harm) that they could but do not prevent. For instance, if I fail to feed my children out of laziness or spite, then I would be held morally responsible for their suffering even though I do not physically cause their hunger. I would be blamed for my failure to prevent their suffering. This feature of moral responsibility raises a number of interesting philosophical questions about agents and causation that I cannot address here. (Are omissions a special sort of action or are they something distinct? Do omissions cause outcomes, and if so, in what way?) What is important to note is that however one answers these questions, it is clear that we blame people for the outcomes of both their acts and their omissions. In the context of personal responsibility for health, this is perhaps most evident in the emphasis on preventive medicine and health promotion, We assign blame not only for behaviors that cause or increase the risk of illness and injury—smoking or excessive alcohol consumption, for example—but also for failing to act in ways that might have prevented illness or injury—such as for not exercising, not wearing seatbelts, not having mammograms, not receiving regular checkups, not being immunized.

On the other hand, attention to agency narrows the scope of responsibility to outcomes and events that we bring about (or fail to prevent) voluntarily, for it is only when we are acting voluntarily that we are acting as agents. Questions and assumptions about what constitutes voluntary behavior lie just below many controversies over personal responsibility for health. Take, for instance, the debate about whether patients whose liver disease is attributable to alcohol abuse, but who are now abstinent, should have the same access to liver transplantation as patients whose liver failure is not attributable to alcohol abuse. Physicians Alvin Moss and

Mark Siegler have argued that patients with alcohol-related end stage liver disease should be given lower priority as candidates for liver transplantation than patients who are not responsible for their liver disease. (19) Their argument is not that patients are morally responsible for their alcoholism, but rather for the failure to seek effective treatment. Why? Because alcoholism, as a disease, is not voluntarily chosen, whereas the decision to seek or not seek treatment is something over which people do have control. Not surprisingly, critics of this position have responded, in part, by questioning Moss and Siegler's assumptions about voluntary behavior. (20)

To better understand why determinations of moral responsibility should be considered decisions as much as discoveries, it will be helpful to examine the alternative. As philosopher Marion Smiley describes it, the modern understanding construes moral responsibility as an attribute of moral agents, one they possess independent of worldly considerations such as our values, our reasons for assigning blame, or our actual judgments of blame. According to this perspective, she writes, "individuals are blameworthy not in virtue of our social practice of blaming, but in virtue of their having themselves caused—freely willed—either their own actions or an external state of affairs." (21) In other words, there is a fact about whether a person is morally responsible independent of any judgments we make about whether or not to hold him responsible. It is a fact that we could discover if we had ideal knowledge of whether the person's behavior caused the harm in question and whether it was voluntary. According to this view, after we have rendered our fallible human judgment it still makes sense to ask, "Yes, but was the person 'really' responsible?"

Does anyone really hold to this conception of moral responsibility, either in philosophical or ordinary discourse? The answer is yes, although not always explicitly. In philosophical discourse, the conception is revealed in the distinction drawn between moral responsibility and social liability or legal responsibility. For example, in a passage Smiley quotes, philosopher Joel Feinberg writes,

> A stubborn feeling persists even after legal responsibility has been decided that there is still a problem—albeit not a legal problem—left over: namely, is the defendant really responsible (as opposed to "responsible in law") for the harm? This conception of a "real" theoretical responsibility distinct from a practical responsibility "relative" to the purposes and values of a particular community is expressed very commonly in the terminology of "morality"—moral obligation, moral guilt, moral responsibility (p. 30).

It is more difficult to know whether ordinary discourse endorses this conception of moral responsibility because people often do not make their presuppositions clear. However, I think there is ample, if indirect, evidence that this conception is common. The evidence consists of two interrelated tendencies found in discussions of personal responsibility for health. The first is the failure to clearly distinguish between moral responsibility and causality. The second, although there are notable exceptions, is that attributions of moral responsibility are often made as if they were given or unproblematic. The result is that the individual's moral responsibility for illness, injury, or health risk is often presented as if it were an established fact that had already been discovered.

Consider an argument, made by Eike Henner Kluge in the Canadian Medical Association Journal. (22) She argues that people who make "medically inappropriate lifestyle choices," such as decisions to smoke or to drink alcohol, do not have the same right to health care as people who choose not to smoke or drink. Her argument is straightforward. People create (which is to say cause) preventable health care needs by smoking or drinking. People have control over their decisions to smoke or drink. Therefore they, not society, should be responsible for their preventable health care needs. "[T]o smoke," she writes, "is to create an artificial and preventable health need. That is irresponsible, and to insist that smokers be treated like nonsmokers is to unjustly treat irresponsible people as responsible people" (p. 746). What is interesting is that Kluge seems to believe that the argument really hinges on only one simple question: Do people have control over whether to smoke or drink? Her answer is an unequivocal yes. She acknowledges that other factors (such as environment and genetic predisposition) contribute to such behaviors, but dismisses them as irrelevant as long as persons have some control. Thus people who make inappropriate lifestyle choices are morally responsible in virtue of their having created—caused (freely willed, Smiley would say)—their health care needs. The determination of responsibility depends entirely on the person being judged. Even though the question of moral responsibility is being asked in the context of the practical problem of allocating health care resources, there is no indication that how or why we are assessing responsibility affects the fact of responsibility at all.

There are several reasons to believe that this understanding of moral responsibility is inadequate and should be abandoned in favor of a more pragmatic one. Here, however, I will only suggest two.

First, as a practical matter, we must set limits on the scope of responsibility that are not entailed by the theoretical concept of moral responsibility alone. The world is full of troubles; there are many harms that I conceivably could but do not prevent. What are the limits of my responsibility? What harms am I morally responsible for? There are many possible replies to these questions. Any moral theory must address them, for no plausible theory could hold us morally accountable for all the harms that we could but do not prevent. One possibility would be to develop an abstract and general theory of moral obligation that would allow us to distinguish, in any given situation, between harms that we are obligated to prevent and harms that we are not obligated to prevent. However, notice what happens when we ask the question in a slightly different way. Suppose we ask, "what harms can I be expected to prevent? What risks should I be expected to avoid?" A different, more pragmatic approach then suggests itself. The emphasis shifts from the theoretical to the practical. The expectations that define the limits of moral responsibility will depend on the particular contexts in which we hold people responsible, and thus on our interests, values, and social practices.

The types of social practices and contexts that shape these expectations pertaining to moral responsibility are varied. Some moral responsibilities are attached to specific social roles—physician, nurse, patient, parent, or teacher—and the special relationships that arise from them. Although health affects everyone, it is plausible to think that even our expectations regarding health and health-related behaviors may be attached to certain social roles. For instance, we may expect professional athletes to devote great attention to their health and fitness, or patients to conscientiously follow the advice of health care professionals. We might even expect parents with dependent children to modify their health-related behavior in light of their parental responsibilities.

Other moral responsibilities arise from more general social norms. What we are personally expected to do or refrain from doing in order to promote our health depends, in part, on how our society values health relative to other goods such as personal freedom, recreation, or even culinary delight. Finally, particular social contexts also shape our expectations concerning personal responsibility for health. It is hard to deny that a good deal of the recent emphasis on personal responsibility for health stems from the rising cost of health care and the mechanisms that we use to finance health care. The need to pool resources in order to pay for health care creates moral responsibilities for health and illness that would probably not exist if health care were inexpensive enough to be paid for individually.

The distribution of power is another contingent feature of particular social contexts that plays an important role in shaping expectations and, thus, assigning moral responsibility. An illustration of how power can affect the attribution of responsibility for health to individuals is found in Jonathan Moreno and Ronald Bayer's account of the history behind mandatory seat belt laws. (23) The failure of safety campaigns to motivate drivers to use seat belts led, in the 1970s and '80s, to proposals that would have forced manufacturers to include air bags or automatic seat belts as mandatory equipment. Faced with the prospect of regulation and expensive redesign, the automotive industry invested $15 million in a campaign aimed at getting states to pass mandatory seat belt laws. This effort, in effect, shifted the responsibility for health and safety from the manufacturers back onto individuals. (24)

More recently, the legal and political struggle over tobacco settlements can be seen, in part, as a public debate about how to assign responsibility for the burdens created by smoking. For many years the tobacco lobby has been able to keep the burden primarily on individual smokers. However, the recent trend of holding tobacco companies more liable reflects a shift in power from the tobacco industry toward plaintiffs. It is arguable that this shift is not a consequence of any new scientific development, but of the ability of states' attorneys general to move the focus from issues of smokers' individual health and responsibility to the financial impact of smoking on states' budgets. (25) Both cases reflect shifts in social liability; neither could have occurred without corresponding changes in attributions of moral responsibility.

The second reason we should consider claims of moral responsibility to be as much decisions as discoveries arises from the problematic notion of free or voluntary action. As I have described the concept of moral responsibility, a claim that a person is blameworthy is based on a prior judgment that the person acted voluntarily. Thus if there is to be an independent fact regarding moral responsibility, then there must be an independent fact regarding voluntary behavior. But independent facts regarding voluntary behavior have proved illusive. At a theoretical level we lack any consensus on a philosophically adequate notion of free will that would allow us to determine, as a matter of fact, whether an action is voluntary or not. At a more practical level we utilize different and competing explanatory models to explain behavior. Veatch, for instance, notes that there are at least four different models—the voluntary, medical, psychological, and social-structural—that could be used to answer the question of whether health risks are voluntary. (26)

Since we lack agreement about what voluntary behavior is, when we make a judgment about whether a person acted freely we are expressing a standard or expectation of self-control rather than a discovery of fact. Our social practices, as well as our scientific understanding, shape these expectations. The social practice of blaming is expressive—it shapes our notion of free will. What we consider a free action depends to a large extent on what we are willing to hold people responsible for. This has led at least one philosopher to advocate drawing cautious conclusions about personal responsibility for health. "[P]ending further enlightenment from philosophical theory," he writes, "we must despair of a firm answer. . . . [I]n each set of firmly held opinions, there is usually more ideology than philosophy." (27)

Causal Responsibility

Now one might agree that there is no simple independent fact about whether a person is socially liable or morally responsible for his health, but nevertheless argue that there is such a fact about whether the person is causally responsible for his health. Whether a person is causally responsible for his health is a fact that we can and must discover independent of our reasons for holding people responsible. I think this view is seriously flawed. Determinations of causality, like determinations of social liability or moral responsibility, are unavoidably dependent on us—on our values, social practices, and practical considerations. They too are as much decisions as discoveries.

Let me try to defend my claim about the nature of causality by considering the commentaries accompanying two studies of the correlation between body mass and mortality published in the *New England Journal of Medicine* during the late 1990s. (28) While both studies confirmed what has been widely suspected, namely that obesity increases the risk of mortality, the accompanying commentaries cautioned against emphasizing weight loss strategies designed for individuals. Jerome Kassirer and Marcia Angell drew attention to the ineffectiveness of many weight loss programs, the need to balance the modest benefits of weight loss against both the financial costs and health risk of weight loss programs, and the dangerous eating disorders that are encouraged by our cultural obsession with weight.

More radically, perhaps, David Williamson called into question the strategy of targeting individual behavior as a way of controlling obesity. "The large community-based trials of methods for the prevention of heart disease," he wrote,

> demonstrated that targeting individual behavior was ineffective in reducing the prevalence of cardiovascular disease and obesity, and this finding has motivated a search for new public health interventions emphasizing environmental change (e.g., adding more sidewalks and parks, promoting physical activity in the workplace). Some physicians may believe that, in dealing with obesity, environmental change is outside their purview. In tobacco control, however, the role of physicians in promoting environmental change is becoming well recognized. (29)

To show how these commentaries support my claim that determinations of causality are as much decision as discovery I need to draw attention to a feature of causal explanations that is sometimes overlooked, their indeterminacy. Causal explanations contain an implicit ceteris paribus clause, a proviso that the explanation holds "all other features of the situation being normal." These other features include other possible causal factors that we relegate to the background. Thus, determining causality for any state of affairs involves a decision—a selection process in which we highlight certain causal factors and relegate others to the background.

Consider the question, "what is the cause of obesity?" Body weight may be influenced by a number of factors, including heredity, lifestyle and behavior, and social and physical environment. If we say that lifestyle causes obesity, then we are saying that lifestyle influences obesity, given certain normal assumptions about heredity and the social and physical environment. But how do we decide what causes obesity—that is, which factors to identify as "the cause" (or causes) and which to relegate to the ceteris paribus clause? The decision cannot be determined solely by the relationship between the causal factors and the effect in question; it depends on practical considerations, and thus on the context in which the causal explanation is offered. (30)

Here are two of many practical considerations that are relevant to assignments of responsibility for health to individuals: effectiveness and the structure of social institutions. The first of these has to do with our ability to control situations and events. Identifying the cause of an illness, for instance, involves answering the question, "How will identifying factor X, as opposed to Y or Z, as a cause help us control or prevent the illness?" Identifying causes in this sense was what R.G. Collingwood argued natural science, in as much as it is a practical science, is all about. The "'cause' of an event in nature," he wrote, "is the handle, so to speak, by which we can manipulate it." (31) It is interesting to note that the commentaries focused on the inadequacy of the individualistic approach to combating obesity. Practical considerations are at the forefront. If social and environmental factors are better "handles" for controlling obesity, then they merit greater consideration. It is time to bring them forward.

Of course, one might argue that the connection between handles and causes need not imply that practical considerations determine our assessment of causality. (32) In fact, it might be claimed that the structure of dependence is reversed from what I have just presented. Ordinarily we do not believe that factor X is a cause of event Y because it is a handle by which we can manipulate Y; we believe that X is a handle because it is a cause of Y. At some level this debate about the relationship between handles and causes is not resolvable; it is a debate about basic metaphysical presuppositions. However, if we restrict ourselves to knowledge claims that we can establish through science, it is clear that handles are the key to identifying causes. How, after all, would one know, or be able to prove, that X causes Y if one could not manipulate X? (33)

Understanding causes as handles has two important implications. First, our ability to control situations and events, and thus our attribution of causality, is relative to the state of our knowledge and technological capabilities. Second, when we find a new or better handle for a problem, and thus shift attributions of causality, we may shift attributions of moral responsibility as well. Williamson's public health approach, while it does not completely eliminate the individual's responsibility, places responsibility on other parties as well. A hint at who might also be considered morally responsible can be found in the list of other parties he encourages physicians to enlist as partners in the battle against obesity—food marketers and manufacturers, transportation agencies, urban planners, and others.

Williamson's claim that many physicians are reluctant to address environmental causes of obesity because they lie "outside their purview" suggests another practical consideration that affects our selection of causes—the structure of our social institutions and practices and the location of problems relative to them. Why have we focused largely on individual behaviors and remedies in regard to obesity? In part because we have viewed obesity as a medical problem, and the institution of medicine is structured to focus on the individual patient. It is not surprising that someone interested in public health pays greater attention to social and environmental factors. (At the time Williamson wrote his commentary, he was associated with the Center for Disease Control and Prevention.) The social institutions we participate in, such as medicine and public health, shape our values, assumptions, explanatory models, and problem-solving approaches. Thus they also influence our causal explanations. There is some truth to the saying that if you are a carpenter with a hammer, every problem looks like a nail. In part, then, the determination of whether lifestyle causes obesity is a decision that depends on what social institution is asked to address the problem.

Stephen Toulmin makes this point in his discussion of medical causation. Because medicine is a practical enterprise, he argues, the way in which causation is discussed within it will "reflect current assumptions about responsibility for bringing about or preventing medical outcomes, and thus current views about the acceptable and effective loci of intervention." (34) These assumptions will in turn be influenced by ideas about the proper scope of medical practice and the physician's professional role, both of which are largely formed by the ways in which physicians (and other health professionals) are professionalized. What is particularly interesting about Toulmin's argument is that it leads to the conclusion that causal responsibility is, in some respects, dependent on assessments of moral responsibility and not merely vice versa. (35)

I have tried to suggest that effectiveness and the structure of social institutions are two of many practical considerations that contribute to determinations of causal responsibility for health. I am sure that more could be identified. However, if such considerations play a significant role in determining what we identify as the cause of an illness, then responsibility for health is not a simple fact about the world that can be discovered through scientific and medical research alone. We decide who and what are responsible for health, both morally and causally, by appealing to a complex constellation of our values, goals, interests, and social practices.

Into the Public Realm

As we gain more knowledge about the relationship between health and lifestyle, and as the competition for limited health care resources intensifies, questions about personal responsibility for health will emerge more frequently. These questions cannot be objectively or conclusively answered through scientific and medical research alone. The answers will be dependent on us—on our values, our social practices and institutions, and our reasons for holding people responsible. This raises a new concern. If scientific and medical research cannot provide objective substantive assessments, how can we avoid making decisions that are arbitrary or discriminatory?

While I have not argued for it in this paper, I believe the answer is to shift our attention from substantive to procedural solutions. Only by using processes of public deliberation in which our values, goals, and interests are exposed to scrutiny and discussion can we both avoid arbitrary and discriminatory decisions. (36) While we cannot determine, as a simple, independent matter of fact, whether persons are responsible either for their behavior or their health, we may nevertheless be able to decide together, in a fair and impartial manner, when we should hold them responsible.

Acknowledgements

I would like to thank Seton Hall University for providing a Summer Research Grant that allowed me to work on this article. I also want to thank Martin Benjamin, Len Fleck, Tom Tomlinson, Yvonne Unna, and the anonymous reviewers, all of whom provided valuable feedback at various stages in the project.

References

(1.) L. Gannet, "What's in a Cause? The Pragmatic Dimension of Genetic Explanations," *Biology and Philosophy* 14 (1999): 349–74. Gannett notes that one of the justifications for spending billions of dollars on the human genome research is the belief that genes are key determinants of disease.

(2.) R.M. Veatch, "Voluntary Risks to Health," *Journal of the American Medical Association* 243, no. 1 (1980): 50–55, at 52.

(3.) F. Fitzgerald, "The Tyranny of Health," *NEJM* 331, no. 3 (1994): 196–98, at 196. See also H. Becker, "The Tyranny of Health Promotion," *Public Health Reviews* 14 (1986): 15–25.

(4.) Jeff Kahn cites a 1993 *USA Today*/CNN poll that showed that 83 percent of the public supported increased tobacco taxes as a means of financing health care reform. J. Kahn, "Sin Taxes as a Mechanism of Health Care Finance: Moral and Policy Considerations," in *Allocating Health Care Resources*, ed. J.M. Humber and R.F. Almeder (Totowas, N.J.: Humana Press, 1995), 179–202.

(5.) For discussion of liver transplantation for alcoholics see C. Cohen and M. Benjamin, "Alcoholics and Liver Transplantation," *JAMA* 265 (1991): 1299–301; M. Benjamin and J.G. Turcotte, "Ethics, Alcoholism, and Liver Transplantation," in *Liver Transplantation and the Alcoholic Patient*, ed. M.R. Lucey et al. (Cambridge: Cambridge University Press, 1994), 113–30; and A.H. Moss and M. Siegler, "Should Alcoholics Compete Equally for Liver Transplantation?" *JAMA* 265, no. 10 (1991): 1295–97. For an argument that lifestyle considerations provide an appropriate basis for refusing someone a donated organ as well as access to other scarce health care resources see E.H. Kluge, "Drawing the Ethical Line Between Organ Transplantation and Lifestyle Abuse," *Canadian Medical Association Journal* 150, no. 5 (1994): 745–46.

(6.) For more on policies implemented by employers to influence the lifestyles of employees see American Civil Liberties Union, "Lifestyle Discrimination," Workplace Rights (1998): http://www.aclu.org/issues/worker/ legkit5.html.

(7.) Smoking provides a good example. For the discussion of whether smokers should be denied access to coronary bypass surgery in Great Britain see M.J. Underwood and J.S. Bailey, "Should Smokers Be Offered Coronary Bypass Surgery?" *British Medical Journal* 306 (1993): 1047–1050; M.I. Khalid, "Denying Treatment is Indefensible," *British Medical Journal* 306 (1993): 1408; and N. Mamode, "Denying Access is More Costly," *British Medical Journal* 306 (1993): 1408.

(8.) For discussion of holding patients responsible for noncompliance see C. Cassel and J. La Puma, Commentary on "The Noncompliant Substance Abuser," *Hastings Center Report 21*, no. 2 (1991): 30–31; L. Stell, Commentary on "The Noncompliant Substance Abuser," *Hastings Center Report* 21, no. 2 (1991): 31–32; and D. Orentlicher, "Denying Treatment to the Noncompliant Patient," *JAMA* 265, no. 12 (1991): 1579–82.

(9.) Michigan State University, Healthy U Health Letter (Spring 1998). The minutes are estimated for a 150-pound person jogging eleven-minute miles.

(10.) K.D. Brownell, "Personal Responsibility and Control Over Our Bodies: When Expectation Exceeds Reality," *Health Psychology* 10, no. 5 (1991): 303–310.

(11.) Other philosophers who provide moral general analyses of moral responsibility identify different senses. For example, see G. Dworkin, "Taking Risks, Assessing Responsibility," *Hastings Center Report* 11, no. 5 (1981): 26–31. The senses identified here are those that are most frequently run together in discussion of personal responsibility for health.

(12.) Dworkin refers to this sense of responsibility as "liability-responsibility": "It is the claim that judgments or actions are warranted as a response to some faulty aspect of a person's conduct." Dworkin, "Taking Risks," 28.

(13.) For discussion of justifications for lifestyle proposals see D. Wikler, "Personal Responsibility for Illness" in *Health Care Ethics*, ed. D. Van De Veer and T. Regan (Philadelphia, Pa.: Temple University Press, 1987), 326–58; D. Wikler, "Who Should be Blamed for Being Sick?" *Health Education Quarterly* 14, no. 1 (1987): 11–25; and D. Wilker and D.E. Beauchamp, "Lifestyles and Public Health," in *The Encyclopedia of Bioethics*, ed. W.T. Reich (New York: Simon & Schuster Macmillan, 1995), 1366–69.

(14.) W. James, *Pragmatism*, ed. Bruce Kuklick (Indianapolis, Ind.: Hackett Publishing Company, 1981), 33.

(15.) For a pragmatic analysis of moral responsibility see M. Smiley, *Moral Responsibility and the Boundaries of Community: Power and Accountability from a Pragmatic Point of View* (Chicago, Ill.: University of Chicago Press, 1992).

(16.) A pragmatic interpretation of objectivity will rely on the notions of inter-subjective agreement, reasonableness, and making sense. For more discussion of pragmatic conceptions of objectivity see D. DeGrazia, *Taking Animals Seriously: Mental Life and Moral Status* (Cambridge: Cambridge University Press, 1996); R. Rorty, "Solidarity or Objectivity?" in *Objectivity, Relativism, and Truth* (Cambridge: Cambridge University Press, 1991), 21–34; and H. Putnam, "Objectivity and the Science/Ethics Distinction," in *Realism with a Human Face* (Cambridge: Harvard University Press, 1990), 163–78.

(17.) For more thorough analyses of moral responsibility see J. Feinberg, *Doing and Deserving* (Princeton, NJ: Princeton University Press, 1970); P.A. French, *Responsibility Matters* (Lawrence, Kan.: University of Kansas Press, 1992); M. Walker, "Geographies of Responsibility" *Hastings Center Report* 27, no. 1 (1997): 38–44.

(18.) Kluge, "Drawing the Ethical Line"; Persaud's, "Smokers' Rights to Health Care"; and T.M. Powledge, "No Smoking: New Sanctions for Old Habits," *Hastings Center Report* 8, no. 2 (1978): 11–12.

(19.) Moss and Seigler, "Should Alcoholics Compete."

(20.) Cohen and Benjamin, "Alcoholics and Liver Transplantation," and Benjamin and Turcotte, "Ethics, Alcoholism, and Liver Transplantation."

(21.) Smiley, *Moral Responsibility*, 6. For more on this conception of moral responsibility see pp. 72–101.

(22.) Kluge, "Drawing the Ethical Line."

(23.) J.D. Moreno and R. Bayer, "The Limits of the Ledger in Public Health Promotion," *Hastings Center Report* 15, no. 6 (1985): 37–41.

(24.) For an example that reflects a Marxist interpretation see R. Crawford, "You Are Dangerous to Your Health: The Ideology and Politics of Victim Blaming," *International Journal of Health Services* 7, no. 4 (1977): 663–80. Crawford argues that we should understand attempts to assign responsibility for illness to individuals as an ideologically motivated class strategy to divert attention from the social and industrial causes of illness.

(25.) I am indebted to the reviewers who pointed out to me the role that state attorneys general played in this shift of social liability.

(26.) Veatch, "Voluntary Risks to Health."

(27.) Wikler, "Personal Responsibility," 341.

(28.) The commentaries are J.P. Kassirer and M. Angell, "Losing Weight—An Ill-Fated New Year's Resolution," *NEJM* 338, no. 1 (1998): 52–54; and D.E Williamson, "The Prevention of Obesity," *NEJM* 341, no. 15 (1999): 1140–141. The studies are J. Stevens et al, "The Effect of Age on the Association between Body-mass Index and Mortality," *NEJM* 338, no. 1 (1998): 1–7; and E. Calle et al., "Body-mass Index and Mortality in a Prospective Cohort of U.S. Adults," *NEJM* 341, no. 15 (1999): 1097–105.

(29.) Williamson, "The Prevention of Obesity," 1141.

(30.) For pragmatic accounts of causal explanation see R.G. Collingwood, "On the So-Called Idea of Causation," *Proceedings of the Aristotelian Society* 38 (1938): 85–112; S. Toulmin, "Causation and the Locus of Medical Intervention," in *Changing Values in Medicine*, ed. E.J Cassell and M. Siegler (Lanham, Md.: University Publications of America, Inc, 1979), pp. 59–72; and B. van Frassen, *The Scientific Image* (Oxford: Clarendon Press, 1980). See also Gannet, "What's in a Cause?" Toulmin and Gannet's articles are particularly relevant to this discussion in that they focus on causation in the medical context.

(31.) Collingwood, "On the So-Called Idea of Causation," 89.

(32.) I am indebted to the anonymous reviewer who brought this objection to my attention.

(33.) It should be noted that I am using "manipulate" very broadly here. Manipulating a potential causal factor does not necessarily mean changing it physically. Manipulating can also be statistical. That is, we may be able to identify a particular gene or behavior as a causal factor in disease without ever changing it if we can statistically correlate the presence of the genetic marker or behavior with the disease.

(34.) Toulmin, "Causation and the Locus of Medical Intervention," 66.

(35.) This coincides well with the claim made by many pragmatists that there is no clear distinction between facts and values. Hilary Putnam has been particularly articulate on this issue. See H. Putnam, "The Place of Facts in a World of Values," in *Realism with a Human Face* (Cambridge, Mass.: Harvard University Press, 1990), 163–78; H. Putnam, "Fact and Value" in *Pragmatism: A Reader*, ed. L. Menand (New York: Vintage Books, 1997), 338–62; H. Putnam, "Beyond the Fact/Value Dichotomy" in *Realism with a Human Face* (Cambridge, Mass.: Harvard University Press, 1990), 163–78.

(36.) I think the process of rational democratic deliberation defended by Leonard Fleck and others holds promise, but more work must be done to see how it could be implemented in situations that do not involve government institutions, such as insurance plans and places of employment. See L. Fleck, "Just Caring: Oregon, Health Care Rationing, and Informed Democratic Deliberation," *Journal of Medicine and Philosophy* 19 (1994): 367–88; L. Fleck, "Just Health Care Rationing: A Democratic Decisionmaking Approach," *University of Pennsylvania Law Review* 140, no. 5 (1992): 1597–636; and L. Fleck, "Justice, HMOs, and the Invisible Rationing of Health Care Resources," *Bioethics* 4, no. 2 (1990): 97120.

Scot D. Yoder, "Individual Responsibility for Health: Decision, not Discovery," *Hastings Center Report* 32, no. 2 (2002): 22–31.

Scot D. Yoder is a visiting assistant professor at Michigan State University. His research interests include practical philosophy, pragmatism and medical ethics, and the relationship between business and medical ethics.

Your Liver Will Keep You Alive

Madison Memorial Hospital, Madison, WI

If asked to name one word you most associate with liver disease, you'd probably say "alcohol." Alcohol abuse does in fact contribute to about 20,000 liver-related deaths every year, but there are numerous other causes of liver disease, and viral hepatitis may be an equal or greater threat to life and good health.

The largest internal organ, weighing up to four pounds, the liver acts as the body's food and drug administration—regulating chemicals and eliminating toxins. It's an essential and very complex organ, performing more than 500 functions in the body, including

- manufacturing the bile necessary for digestion,
- processing and regulating blood levels of carbohydrates, fats and protein,
- cleansing the blood of toxic substances,
- breaking down alcohol and other drugs,
- storing excess vitamins and minerals;
- regulating the clotting action of blood,
- controlling the production of cholesterol and
- helping the body resist infection.

Located in the upper abdominal cavity, the liver is partially protected by the lower rib cage but because of its position, its large size and the way it moves within the body, it's particularly vulnerable to injury.

Once wounded, whether by a blow or puncture, it has an additional risk of being injured by the ribs.

After a trauma, your liver will likely require medical attention; a bleeding liver must be patched or sewn up. Bleeding of the liver is characterized by sudden, sharp abdominal pain, shortness of breath, a quick pulse and sometimes dizziness.

Although the liver is generally resilient, the only human organ able to regenerate itself, it's also vulnerable to a number of diseases.

Signs of Liver Disease

Common signs of liver disorders include jaundice or yellowing of the skin and the whites of the eyes; dark urine; light-colored stool; easy bleeding; persistent itching; small, spider-like blood vessels in the skin and accumulation of fluid in the abdominal cavity, known as ascites. Since the liver is responsible for removing toxins from the body, a person with liver problems may also show signs of cloudy thinking, confusion or mood changes.

The distended abdomen, red nose, broken blood vessels and impaired judgment of the alcoholic can be attributed in part to an impaired liver. In some cases, the damaged liver can recover, at least to some extent, with treatment and abstention from alcohol. Cirrhosis, or the scarring that occurs from chronic inflammation of the liver, however, cannot be reversed.

Hepatitis, a viral inflammation of the liver, is the leading cause of liver disease and cirrhosis worldwide, and several million Americans are infected with one of the hepatitis viruses.

Hepatitis A is easily acquired through contaminated water or food. Since it's eliminated from the body through feces, the hepatitis A virus is frequently spread by restaurant workers and others who are not diligent about washing their hands after going to the toilet. Rarely, however, is the disease serious enough to cause severe or chronic liver problems.

Hepatitis B, a much more dangerous strain, is spread through contact with blood or bodily fluids, including urine, semen, vaginal secretions and even tears and saliva.

Vaccines are available for hepatitis A and B but not for hepatitis C. Also spread by household contact, hepatitis C is the leading indicator for liver transplants, affecting four million persons in the United States alone.

Hepatitis B and C can cause long-term liver problems, sometimes with few or no obvious symptoms. And there are more than a million Americans who carry hepatitis B and can spread it to others without having the disease themselves. Untreated hepatitis is the most common reason for liver failure, and these individuals also have an elevated risk of liver cancer.

Numerous cases of severe liver damage are the result of abuse or misuse of street drugs or prescription or over-the-counter medications.

Acute liver failure is a rapid mass destruction of liver cells. Within two weeks, a previously healthy liver can cease to perform its most basic functions.

Early symptoms of liver failure may be ambiguous and variable. Complaints of nausea, fatigue, and loss of appetite are common. Liver function tests are key in indicating liver damage. Without a transplant, up to 80 percent of patients with acute liver failure die.

Dealing with the Organ Shortage

Since the first successful human liver transplantation in 1968, advances in medical technology and surgical techniques have significantly increased the success rate, making it standard therapy for many severe liver disorders as well as acute liver failure.

The highest risks—including organ rejection, infection and surgical complications—occur in the first month after transplantation. After this time, the patient's outlook is typically very good, with survival rates after one and five years of 81 percent and 66 percent, respectively. Many patients are able to return to normal, active life with a greatly improved quality of life.

Unfortunately, the availability of organs from cadavers has diminished in recent years, and supply is insufficient to meet the demand of patients in need of liver transplantation.

One possible approach is to better utilize the currently available supply of donor livers by using "marginal" livers, livers that may not previously have been considered suitable for transplantation, and by splitting an adult liver and sharing the segments between two recipients. Since the human liver is capable of regenerating itself, a segment is capable of growing to near full size within six months.

Because of the increased risk involved and a lack of available facilities, segment transplantation is not widely practiced outside the United States.

Segment transplantation is also possible with living donors. This method was developed primarily in Japan, where cadaveric donation was previously precluded by law. With a healthy living donor, a slightly lower liver volume ratio (40 percent) is acceptable.

Some have suggested establishing degrees of priority for transplantation. Alcoholic liver disease is the main indication for liver transplantation in men and the second most common overall. Since alcoholic patients have damaged their livers through their own actions, some argue that they should not receive the same priority for liver transplantation as others. Also questioned is whether alcoholic patients can benefit to the same degree as non-alcoholics from liver transplantation and whether they are capable of maintaining abstinence and avoiding damage to the transplanted liver.

The best approach, of course, is to be conscious of your liver's health. The liver is a hard-working organ which will keep you healthy if you follow a sensible lifestyle and avoid unnecessary exposure to chemicals, drugs, toxins and hepatitis viruses.

References

Peggy Hollingsworth-Fridlund and Karen Schade, "Collaborative Model: Non-operative Spleen and Liver Management," *Journal of Trauma Nursing*, January, 2000.

Joanne Krumburger, "When the Liver Fails," *RN*, February, 2002.

"Liver Tests," *Mayo Clinic Health Letter*, May, 2000.

Paul McMaster, "Transplantation for Alcoholic Liver Disease in an Era of Organ Shortage," *The Lancet*, February 5, 2000.

M.I. Prince and M. Hudson, "Liver Transplantation for Chronic Liver Disease: Advances and Controversies in an Era of Organ Shortages," *Postgraduate Medical Journal*, March, 2002.

Guard Your Genetic Data from Those Prying Eyes

Dana Hawkins

Seven vials of blood is a lot. That was Janice Avary's first thought when she heard that her husband Gary's employer, the Burlington Northern Santa Fe railroad, was requiring that amount of blood to be taken after he filed claims for a carpal-tunnel injury. As a registered nurse in Alma, Neb., Avary says, her internal alarm was tripped. When she called the company for an explanation, Avary was stunned to hear the words "genetic test."

Her queries led a railroad workers union this month to sue, seeking an end to the allegedly secret testing. BNSF says it has stopped the yearlong pilot program, but Gary Avary thinks that if his wife hadn't asked, it would still be going on. "Unless you have a medical background, you wouldn't know to ask these questions," says Janice Avary.

DNA bias. The lawsuit—the first of its kind against a private employer—was filed just as scientists first published the map of the human genetic code. While genetic advances will likely lead more patients to seek cures for inherited diseases, they are also increasing worries among legal experts and patient rights groups about how genetic data will be used, both in the workplace and elsewhere. "There's no question some employers are testing," says Michael Werner, a lawyer for Bio, a group representing the biotech industry. "And as more tests are developed and the price drops, the market is expected to grow." Even so, there are ways to protect your privacy in the workplace—or if you choose to be tested on your own.

A big concern among genetic experts is that results from such tests could be used to block someone from being hired or promoted, or to deny insurance. Already, there are hundreds of documented cases alleging genetic discrimination by employers and insurers. For example, preliminary results from a survey by the Genetic Alliance, a coalition of patient advocacy groups, show that 42 percent of 220 respondents claimed health insurance discrimination. Sixteen percent cited bias at work and in the military. The survey included such cases as a woman who alleged she was denied long-term disability insurance because the company said she had a predisposition for Alzheimer's disease. Its decision was based on a doctor's scribbled notation in her medical record that her father might have the condition. In another instance, after a first grader was diagnosed with a genetic developmental disorder, his mother's employer eliminated the child's healthcare coverage, saying the diagnosis qualified as a pre-existing condition.

Protect yourself. While federal workers are legally protected against genetic bias in health insurance and employment, private employees are not. Rep. Louise

Slaughter, a New York Democrat, says support is building for legislation she cosponsored this month that would ban such discrimination. "Each of us has bad genes, and eventually they'll all be identified with diseases," says Slaughter. Even some genetic experts who advocate responsible testing, like Vivian Weinblatt, president of the National Society of Genetic Counselors, are advising patients to consider waiting for Congress to pass such a law before getting screened. "Ask yourself: Will knowing the results make my life better? Will I make different life choices? Can I wait a year?" says Weinblatt. If results will help you to treat or prevent a condition for which you're currently at risk, like colon cancer, testing may be wise. If not, or if the results could be inconclusive, says Weinblatt, then it's probably not worth the risk of a permanent flag on your medical record.

If you decide to test, experts offer this advice: Express any concerns to your physician or a genetic counselor and ask who would have access to your records. Find out whether your employer is self-insured, meaning your boss might get the bills. And consider buying life, health, and disability insurance before getting screened.

Question whether you really need to be tested. In some cases you might consider making the same lifestyle changes you'd make if you tested positive. Those with a family history of breast cancer, for example, might forgo genetic testing and instead be vigilant about regular breast exams. Also, be aware you may learn something you could later regret knowing. For instance, one of the tests for predisposition to heart disease may also reveal a risk for Alzheimer's.

Finally, become familiar with the mechanics of testing. If your employer requires blood samples, get a list of the tests to be run. And ask what happens with the blood afterward: Is it stored or destroyed? The railroad workers are still waiting to find out; their test called for only two blood samples. "What did they do with the other five vials?" asks Janice Avary. She wonders: Were other tests planned?

Tracing Workplace Problems to Hidden Disorders

Peggy Stuart

Neurobiological disorders cause hidden costs to your company in the form of lowered productivity, increased turnover and health care claims. Diagnosis and treatment of these individuals can reduce these costs and improve their quality of life.

You're dreading the interview. Fred is on his way to the office and you still don't know what you're going to say. You know it's his last chance to keep his job. Your mind massages the behaviors, one by one, that have brought him to your attention. You're hoping for some clue to why an obviously bright, capable person would do what he does.

Fred shows flashes of brilliance. The rest of the time he's late finishing his work or does a mediocre job. He has difficulty getting along with his co-workers. His work area is messy and his appearance is unkempt. When his supervisor discusses these problems with him, he's astonished and defensive.

It isn't as if Fred were your only problem employee. You still have to deal with Beth, who has used up all her sick leave and vacation time with minor complaints: headache, stomachache and back pain. Ellen's supervisor has complained that Ellen keeps getting up to check the copier, to make sure she reset it after she used it. She may check it 15 to 20 times. Ellen also is late for work almost every day. Then there's Jeremy, who falls asleep at meetings, and even, sometimes, at his desk. (Is he moonlighting?) What do you do about these unmotivated employees"

There are other problems to deal with, too, such as the complaints about John. His work is fine, but four different employees have expressed concern to you that he may be on drugs. They say he keeps swinging his arms at them, and sometimes yells obscenities for no apparent reason.

The truth is, all these behaviors could be caused by any one or a combination of neurobiological disorders (NBD), a quirk—usually genetic—in the chemistry or in the anatomy of the brain. They are physical disabilities that result in the inability or reduced ability of the person to control his or her behavior, movements, emotions or thoughts.

There are many disorders of this type, including autism and pervasive developmental disorders, schizophrenia, anxiety and panic disorders, but in the workplace you're most likely to see:

1) Attention deficit disorder (ADD, or ADHD if hyperactivity is present): a difficulty in concentrating that produces multiple symptoms, sometimes including hyperactivity

2) Depression: uncontrollable sadness for no apparent reason, clinical depression) or in some people depression alternating with manic, or high-activity states (bi-polar depression)

3) Obsessive-compulsive disorder (OCD): uncontrollable and recurring thoughts or behaviors relating to an unreasonable fear

Peggy Stuart, "Tracing Workplace Problems to Hidden Disorders" in *Personnel Journal*, vol. 71, no. 6, June, 1992, p. 82 (9).

4) Narcolepsy: uncontrollable sleepiness, even after what should be adequate sleep
5) Tourette syndrome (TS): uncontrollable movements or utterances, sometimes even obscenities.

There usually are additional symptoms, some of which are shared by two or more of these disorders. Some individuals have more than one disorder. This makes diagnosis difficult.

If you're managing 500 people, it's possible that nearly 100 of them have at least a mild form of one or more of these disorders. NBDs cost your company in increased medical benefits, absenteeism, reduced productivity and turnover. In fact, Peter Ross, executive director of the National Foundation for Depressive estimates the cost to U.S. businesses from depression alone to be between $27 billion and $35 billion each year.

Although many people who have neurobiological disorders don't know what's wrong with them, some do, and the new Americans with Disabilities Act (ADA) may require you to accommodate them, if necessary, so they can do their jobs, as long as it's reasonably possible to do so. You also can't refuse to hire them, if they can perform the "essential functions" of the job. You must hire them and accommodate them, but, undiagnosed, they'll cost you. Does the situation sound like a Catch 22? It needn't be one. These disorders are physical conditions that are treatable and have a high rate of successful response to treatment.

"Research in the last few years has documented the physical basis of these disorders," says Enid Peschel, co-director, Program for Humanities in Medicine and assistant professor (adjunct) of Internal Medicine at Yale University School of Medicine. "There has been a belief that such disorders as OCD were the result of inner conflicts. Now we know that they result from a malfunction in the basal ganglia of the brain," she adds.

Alan Zametkin, MD, psychiatrist at the National Institute of Mental Health in Bethesda, Maryland, has used positron emission tomography (PET) to study the brains of adults who have ADHD (ADD that includes hyperactivity). He has found that certain parts of the brain that control attention are underactive in persons who have ADHD as compared with normal brains. This helps explain why stimulant medications often help calm these people.

The most successful treatment available today is medication, often combined with support groups or reality-based support, such as training in coping mechanisms. That doesn't mean these people are sedated to prevent the undesirable behavior. The various medications used for these conditions actually correct the malfunction, just as medication is used to correct an irregular heartbeat or high blood pressure. "Medication may not always be able to stop you from hallucinating, but the proper medication often can help even a person who has persistent symptoms to function adequately," Peschel points out. (Most NBD employees you'll see in your work force won't have hallucinations. Although people who do, such as individuals who have depression, or even some who have schizophrenia, may be employable, thanks to medication.)

Medication produces success in varying degrees depending upon the level of severity of the disorder, the individual's biochemistry, and other factors, including a supportive environment. Often the dosage or the choice of medication must people who have these disorders, however, can function normally, or almost normally, after appropriate medication is determined and coping mechanisms have been taught.

David E. Comings, MD, director of the Department of Medical Genetics at the City of Hope National Medical Center in Duarte, California, works with patients who have Tourette Syndrome (TS). He says TS and ADD are closely associated. Between 50% and 80% of his TS patients also have ADD. He estimates that medication in some form is effective 80% to 90% of the time.

Paul H. Wender, MD, professor of psychiatry and director of psychiatric research at the University of Utah Medical Center in Salt Lake City, says, "ADD adults who respond to medication and stay on that medication for a long time get their lives together. There's improvement across all areas. Patients don't become tolerant to medication. The only problem is that many of the drugs that are effective are dealable on the street; amphetamines have been known since 1937 to be effective [for ADD] but Ritalin is usually prescribed," he says.

Because these are controlled substances, doctors are very careful to document their rationale for prescribing them. People who have ADD don't become addicted to the medication, because the biochemical reaction produced isn't the same as that found in people who don't have the disorder, Wender says.

Untreated, NBD adults often become addicted to other substances, however. Joan Andrews, an educational psychologist in Newport Beach, California, who specializes in children and adults who have ADD, estimates that 33% of alcoholics are ADD adults who subconsciously try to self-medicate.

According to Ross, people who have depression also often attempt to self-medicate with alcohol or drugs. Proper treatment of the disorder can prevent substance abuse in these individuals and may be essential if needed chemical dependency treatment is to be successful.

For years these conditions have been treated with various types of psychotherapy. It was believed that NBDs were caused by dysfunctional families or traumatic childhood experiences. Although this treatment sometimes may have been helpful, the basic problem usually returned. "They're in a hole in the ground. If you throw these people a rope—psychotherapy—they climb out and they're fine, but then they revert," Wender says.

Although the NBD disorder itself doesn't respond to psychotherapy, living with such problems for any length of time often creates secondary problems that make counseling in some form beneficial. Training the individual to understand his or her condition is an important part of the treatment, the same as it would be for a person recovering from a heart attack, or learning to live with diabetes. "The patient needs reality-based supportive counseling, the way you work with anyone who has any other chronic physical illness," Peschel says. Ideally, this reality-based supportive counseling should include the family, as well.

When the family becomes involved, other family members may be discovered to have the same disability. This is because these disorders are often genetic. "If a child has ADD, most likely both parents have it in some form or other," says Andrews, who adds that ADD is a recessive trait. (Research at the City of Hope has demonstrated this as well.)

"Usually the family can get along better after treatment. They don't take the person's behavior personally anymore. That helps," says Comings.

This can be true of co-workers, as well. An employee-education program on neurobiological disorders can help you locate these people and help members of the work force understand how to help them.

Employers often can help increase both the productivity and the comfort level in their employees who have neurobiological disorders by making some minor accommodations for them. The accommodations needed vary, depending on the disorder and the individual.

Insurance is another issue. Unfortunately, most insurance plans still call these neurobiological disorders mental health problems and don't cover them on the same level as other physical illnesses. "It would save money if NBD were covered on a par with other physical illnesses. If people aren't treated, the illness gets worse," Peschel says. These are physical problems, but are classified by insurance companies as mental health issues.

Peschel says that one example is Parkinson's disease and schizophrenia. "They're opposite sides of the same coin: Parkinson's disease is associated with too little dopamine, and schizophrenia with an excess of dopamine, yet Parkinson's disease is considered a physical problem (a disease) and schizophrenia a mental one," she points out. If you have a large enough insurance pool, as do many group insurance companies providing corporate health benefits, it needn't be very expensive to make sure these disorders are covered completely, she says.

Some insurance programs won't cover a person at all if he or she has a pre-existing condition. Sometimes the whole family is denied coverage because one person has TS, for example.

The treatment itself can cause problems for the NBD employee. If your company has a drug-testing program, medications used to treat NBD will show up. Employees who are taking medication for a neurobiological disorder should have written statements from their doctors on file, indicating that these drugs are being used for a legitimate purpose. Also, some of these medications must be taken during working hours. The environment at work should make it comfortable for employees who have already-diagnosed neurobiological disorders to make this known.

Fred, Beth, Ellen, Jeremy and John are just five of the nearly 100 people in your work force affected by these disorders. Fred, for instance, has ADD.

Attention deficit disorder. "Often people who have ADD come to me because they're having problems with their jobs. One of the symptoms is disorganization," Andrews says. These people often are underachievers. They work too slowly for their abilities. Their work may be brilliant one day and mediocre the next, but they're unaware that they're doing anything differently. This variable performance is a symptom, she says.

"It's estimated that from 3% to 10% of all children have ADHD (ADD) and that in one-third to two-thirds of these individuals it persists into adult life—that is, at least 1%, and as much as 6% or 7% of the total population," says Wender. These people are distractible and lack concentration. "If they're workers on an oil rig, it doesn't matter." Working on routine paperwork at a desk may be a different matter. They can have volatile mood swings, a hot temper. They're overly reactive. Then they cool down rapidly," he says.

"They're impulsive, from trivial to severe. They interrupt, because they're afraid they're going to forget what they wanted to say. They may buy impulsively, quit jobs for little reason. Some may be physically hyperactive and fidgety," Wender adds.

"They may tell the boss where to go; then the boss tells them where to go," Comings says, so they may change jobs often. "They're poor listeners. They often know what you're going to say before it's out of your mouth."

NBD adults who have achieved white-collar status may have done so because they have developed more successful coping mechanisms or have been fortunate enough to be blessed with high intelligence or family members who keep them on task. "Lower-level employees may have problems different from those of white-collar workers," Andrews says. "They're more likely to have problems with punctuality, personal relationships, problems filling out the time card, jobs that are routine. Many of these people do better outdoors as truck drivers or drilling-rig operators. Inside they feel confined if they're in one spot. They may have depression or mood swings." Often these people are very intelligent. They're just working much below their abilities, she adds.

"On the positive side, they often are very creative, artistic, good with their hands and driven. They can be good employees. Some are workaholics or mildly obsessive-compulsive," says Comings. The difficulty is, these highly driven ADD individuals may go off and start their own businesses. Then you've lost talent and gained competition, he warns.

One odd characteristic of ADD is the way it often disappears when the person is performing an activity he or she likes and finds challenging. Although sitting in one place, performing a simple, routine activity for hours on end is generally difficult or impossible for these people, some of them have no difficulty turning out a complex and thorough report on a subject they like, according to Andrews. Of course, this effect can be observed in most non-ADD individuals, as well. The difference is a matter of degree. Even extreme necessity usually doesn't help the ADD person overcome this difficulty. In fact, adding pressure may make the activity more difficult. When ADD is coupled with high intelligence, finding that challenge becomes an even greater problem, especially in light of the fact that these people may be underemployed.

Fred has an I.Q. of 125. That isn't the only statistic on him that's high. At 40, he's had three marriages and 36 jobs. He's had more traffic tickets than he can count. Still, things could be worse. Some ADD adults end up in our correctional system. Fred is trying to run the race with 20-pound weights around each leg. What can you do to help him? First, refer him to a psychiatrist or psychologist who specializes in neurobiological disorders.

"Approach the employee kindly, tell him or her what you've observed and then recommend someone who can help. Offer hope," Wender recommends. Find a therapist who's pharmacologically sophisticated and can separate the various disorders, because people who display the same behaviors may have entirely different problems. (See "Where To Get Help, page 95.)

Diagnosis is complicated. Although the area of dysfunction shows up on the PET scan, the specific disorder can't be identified. ADD can be identified through a battery of psychometric tests and a lengthy history that includes the patient's description of functioning and symptoms, and descriptions by his or her spouse or other person.

"There are something like 303 different ways ADD can appear. It's like putting together a jigsaw puzzle," Andrews explains. "Younger psychiatrists are aware of the proper treatment for adults who have ADD. It's in the medical textbooks now," she says. An educational psychologist often is good. These people have been diagnosing and treating ADD in children for years. Only in the last 10 years has it been recognized that it can extend into adulthood. The medications used are the same as those prescribed for ADD children, she adds.

If you have an employee who has been exercising heavily on a regular basis, then has to quit for some reason, and begins to have difficulty completing work assignments, there's a possibility that person has ADD. "Exercise may be a form of self-medication," Andrews says. Anyone who has an ADD child should consider being evaluated if he or she has of the symptoms.

Although she says she believes the ADD adult must fit into the workplace, not have the workplace adjusted for him or her, Andrews says there are ways employers can get more out of these employees.

They may need more time to finish assignments or an environment with fewer distractions, she says. Some of them actually concentrate better with a radio playing—others need silence. Things most people can block out during concentration tend to crowd in on the ADD individual and snatch away already-elusive thoughts.

Structuring their work so that they can work on one assignment at a time, perhaps continuing without a break until they finish may be helpful. (Some ADD adults may be nervous and fidgety during a break, when they have nothing to do, and then have difficulty getting back to work.) Setting deadlines for project completion works better for these individuals, who tend to be procrastinators.

Small, tedious tasks should be collected until there are a number of them and then completed all at once. A deadline is good for these, as well. A time-management class or seminar can be helpful if it's especially aimed at the ADD population.

ADD adults often have serious short- and long-term memory problems. Reminding them of anything that's important but routine, when possible, can save a lot of wear and tear on the employee and his or her co-workers and supervisor.

Many people find they can concentrate better on what's going on in a meeting if they take notes, doodle or participate in some other quiet activity as they listen.

Some people participate actively in the discussion to keep their minds from wandering. Find out what specific problems the employee has and work together to find creative solutions.

One ADD businessman was able to solve his credit problem by himself, but kept making poor hiring choices because he was so impulsive that he hired anyone who walked in the door. After he made the hiring process a committee responsibility, the problem was solved, Andrews says. Most of these people can be valued workers, she adds.

Fred most likely has developed a number of coping mechanisms. Some of these may cause problems after Fred is treated for ADD. Others may make him more efficient than other, equally talented individuals. Fred has carried an extra weight around with him all his life. If you can help him to lighten that weight, you may be amazed at what he can do.

Clinical depression. That explains Fred, but what about Beth? Although her symptoms could have another cause, Beth has major depression. Any employee who exhibits a loss of energy and interest, diminished ability to enjoy life, change in sleeping or appetite, or difficulty in concentrating, should be evaluated and treated by a biologically based psychiatrist or physician, as should anyone who appears to be in a manic state, which may appear as a high energy level, an unwarranted or exaggerated belief in one's own ability, extreme irritability or impulsive behavior. (If some of these symptoms seem similar to those of ADD, it's because they are. Correct diagnosis requires expert evaluation.)

Symptoms to Watch For

Any one of these symptoms in itself doesn't mean the employee has a neurobiological disorder. If several of these symptoms are present, he or she should be referred for an evaluation. The correct diagnosis is crucial to determining effective treatment. A skilled diagnostician can rule these disorders out and the person can be referred for psychotherapy, if indicated. Years of psychotherapy will serve little purpose, however, if a neurobiological disorder is left untreated.

Behaviors

Excessive tardiness or absenteeism, poor or inconsistent performance, distractibility, temper outburst, impulsive behavior, poor peer relationships, foul language or other uncontrolled utterances, excessive sleepiness, hoarding, poor stress tolerance, messiness, unkempt appearance, substance abuse, recklessness, mood swings, extreme changes in appetite, forgetfulness frequent physical complaints, persistent sadness, chronic fatigue, loss of interest in activities, isolation, repeated checking activities, superstitious behavior.

Movements

Clumsiness, involuntary movements, physical collapse, fidgeting, muscular weakness, lethargic movement.

Thoughts

Pre-sleep (hypnagogic) hallucinations, recurring thoughts about death, inability to hold a thought, uncontrolled thoughts of one thing, fuzzy thinking.

Other Signs

- A child or other family member diagnosed as having one of these disorders.
- Heavily chapped hands
- Skydiving, gambling, heavy exercise, coupled with behavioral, movement or thought symptoms.

Accommodating an NBD Employee

Mild forms of these disorders may not require an accommodation on the part of the employer, but providing them may improve performance. More severely affected employees may need greater adjustments to their and environment, especially those workers who have attention deficit disorder, obsessive-compulsive disorder, narcolepsy or Tourette syndrome combined with ADD.

The variety of manifestations are as many as the number of individuals who have these disorders. Usually the cost—if any—is small. Find out what problems your employee has and work together to find helpful accommodations. Here are some that may help some people:

- Some people work better on their feet or moving around, at least for part of the day
- Some people have difficulty coping with using the telephone. Reassign telephone duty, if appropriate
- Total quiet or radio background can help some people concentrate
- Some people work better when they have clear deadlines
- An extended lunch period and a place to nap help some
- Some people may work better at home, where they can nap as needed, concentrate without interruptions or avoid worry about venturing outside.
- Allow a person who has ADD to sit in the front row during large meetings. Fellow workers in an audience may be a distraction
- Teach the person to collect routine tasks and then perform all at once at a pre-arranged time
- Provide a forum for the person to share his or her problems with co-workers
- Provide a person the employee can consult as needed to discuss problems as they occur.

Yellowstone to Receive Royalties
Elizabeth G. Daerr

Court Says Park Can Have Bioprospecting Fees

WASHINGTON, D.C.—A federal court has ruled that Yellowstone National Park's 1997 agreement with the Diversa Corporation to share scientific data and royalties from the company's bioprospecting research is valid. Yellowstone's Cooperative Research and Development Agreement (CRADA) is the first of its type made by the National Park Service, and the ruling sets a precedent for other national parks that stand to benefit from similar agreements.

Since 1898, researchers have collected samples from the park's geothermal pools to be used for research purposes, but the park has never benefited from any of the products developed. For example, an enzyme identified in the park in the 1960s was used to develop a process for DNA fingerprinting, which is used for a variety of applications, including identifying criminals and diagnosing cancer. Hoffmann-LaRoche, the company that bought the patent rights to the enzyme, now earns about $100 million annually from it, while Yellowstone receives nothing.

Several groups opposed the CRADA saying that it violated national park regulations and was entered into without proper environmental analysis. The Edmonds Institute, the lead plaintiff in the case, fought the agreement, alleging that the Park Service "is participating in the commercialization and privatization of life." Furthermore, the agreement was made without proper public input, says Beth Burrows, president of the organization.

Under the agreement, Diversa will pay the National Park Service $100,000 over five years and 0.5 percent to 10 percent in royalties for any commercial sales of a product. Any revenue received would be used for research and conservation purposes in Yellowstone.

Judge Royce Lamberth of the U.S. District Court of the District of Columbia wrote in his decision that the agreement was consistent with park statutes and "would produce direct concrete benefits to the park's conservation efforts." Despite the ruling, the agreement continues to be suspended until the park completes an environmental assessment as is required under the National Environmental Policy Act. Because the Park Service's agreement represented a "dramatic change" in national policy, Lamberth said an assessment was necessary. The park began the environmental assessment in February but does not know when it will be completed. In the meantime, Diversa has suspended research until the assessment is complete.

NPCA's Counsel Elizabeth Fayad said the association supports the Park Service's use of this type of profit-sharing agreement, but such arrangements should be entered into only after completion of an environmental analysis.

"The use of CRADA is good public policy, but the Park Service must be certain that any research conducted does not harm the resources or visitors' experience," Fayad said.

Prospecting for Profits

Kari Lydersen

From micro-organisms to Forest Service jobs, privatization hits the national parks. Corporate profits could be enormous; but fragile environments could end up the losers.

Yellowstone, the country's first national park, is home to more geysers and hot springs than anywhere else in the world. Now it is seen as a source of what could be described as organic gold. This "gold" would be the microorganisms that live in Yellowstone's unique ecosystems—like Thermus aquaticus, a heat-loving microbe discovered in the park's Mushroom Pool in 1966.

One of Thermus's enzymes, known as the Taq polymerase, became the key to the polymerase chain reaction technique for manipulating small amounts of genetic material because of its ability to withstand high temperatures. In the 1980s scientist Kary Mullis won the Nobel Prize for perfecting this technique, which has become a key component of molecular biology, medical research and law enforcement, making possible the practice of DNA fingerprinting.

Since buying the patent for the Taq enzyme for $300 million in 1991, the Swiss drug company Hoffman-LaRoche has earned more than $100 million a year from it. Meanwhile Yellowstone and the National Park Service have gotten not a cent from this windfall.

Over the past six years the cash-strapped park service has been planning to change that, with a plan to allow companies to patent microorganisms found in national parks and develop profit-sharing agreements with the park service for their use.

In 1997, at Yellowstone's 125 birthday celebration, the National Park Service and U.S. Department of the Interior announced the signing of a Cooperative Research and Development Agreement (CRADA) with the Diversa Corporation, a San Diego-based company specializing in research in hot springs. Under the plan Diversa would pay Yellowstone $100,000 a year to extract biological tissues, sediment, soil, water and rocks from the park and the park would get a small percent of royalties from any products developed from this research. At the time of the Diversa agreement signing Yellowstone also had at least 15 other similar agreements in the works.

To many in the park service and the corporate world the plan seemed like an ideal fit. Because of the small size of microbial samples—usually an eyedropper or teaspoon of water—this kind of research was not seen as overly invasive. And it could be a way to generate badly needed funds for the park service.

But opposition to the plan quickly surfaced. Critics noted that while Yellowstone should share in profits derived from its resources, the patenting and royalty process creates the temptation for massive prospecting of microbial re-

Kari Lydersen, "Prospecting for Profits" in AlterNet website, July 16, 2003, www.alternet.org/story.html?StoryID=16404.

sources in our nation's parks. And Yellowstone's charter specifically forbids the commercial use of plants and animals from the park.

"Allowing biotechnology companies to extract natural resources from the parks for profit may affect the ability of the parks to serve their inspirational and expressive functions," says a 1999 article in the *Ecology Law Quarterly*. "In deciding to enter into the Diversa agreement, the Park Service has framed the question as whether bioprospecting companies should pay for the right to seek their fortunes in the national parks. The real question, however, is whether they should have that right at all."

In 1998 a lawsuit was filed by the Edmonds Institute, the Alliance for the Wild Rockies, the International Center for Technology Assessment and Montana resident Phil Knight against the U.S. Department of the Interior alleging that the Diversa agreement violated various federal statutes and environmental protections.

While research at Yellowstone and other parks has continued, as a result of the lawsuit this and other CRADA agreements have been stalled pending an environmental assessment study, expected to be released sometime this year.

Patent Profit

Research in Yellowstone or other national parks is nothing new; Yellowstone's first research permit for the collection of microbial materials was issued in 1898 and hundreds of research permits are granted by the park every year.

But the potential for corporations to patent the results of their research and make massive profits off them appears to be escalating. Already enzymes extracted from the hot springs are used for cleaning industrial machines, making paper and beer and tenderizing meat, among other things. And it has been reported that so far only one percent of the microbes in Yellowstone's hot springs have been discovered.

"As the benefits of biotechnology have become increasingly visible, the demand for bioprospecting has also grown," says the lawsuit. "This increased demand places greater and greater value on places like Yellowstone that have a high level of biodiversity, here greater concentrations of genetic information offer the best chance of discovering biochemical materials that may lead to important (and commercially rewarding) projects."

On a large scale the physical process of prospecting for these enzymes could have serious effects on the environment, especially fragile and rare environments like Yellowstone's hot springs. And some see its philosophical implications as even more disturbing—they see it as nothing less than the privatizing and marketing of life.

"You say you're only privatizing microbes, which to most people are what you find squooshed on the bottom of your shoe," said Beth Burrows, executive director of the Edmonds Institute, a Washington-based non-profit public interest group. "But then what's next? Privatizing plants? Animals? Human beings?"

Privatizing Workers

While microorganisms are on the road to being privatized for profit, so are the park service and forest service employees who are charged with protecting the environments that are home to these microorganisms and other diverse forms of plant and animal life.

Under a mandate from President Bush that federal agencies study at least half of all potentially commercial positions for privatization, thousands of park service and forest service jobs along with hundreds of thousands of other federal jobs in various sectors are being considered for privatization. According to the American Federal Government Employees (AFGE) union, the largest federal employees union in the country, 850,000 to one million jobs—or over half the federal workforce—are likely to be privatized in the next few years. This includes park and forest service employees as well as prison guards, border patrol officers, veterans' healthcare providers and more.

In April National Park Service Director Fran Mainella announced that 900 park service jobs are already slated for immediate replacement by private contractors, and in the coming months another 1,323 more jobs will be privatized. These 2,200 plus jobs represent about 13 percent of the Park Service's total workforce, according to the non-profit watchdog group PEER (Public Employees for Environmental Responsibility). The bulk of these jobs are maintenance and administrative positions, though hundreds of scientists, archaeologists and environmentalists are also on the roster for privatization.

Privatization plans for the Forest Service were announced in early July. Forest jobs being privatized include wildfire control, law enforcement, environmental protection and timber production.

And this is just the tip of the iceberg. Over the next three years thousands more park and forest service jobs will also be studied to see if they can be more cheaply filled by private contractors. By the end of fiscal year 2007, the forest service is expected to privatize 10,000 of its 44,000 jobs.

"This will be a fairly radical transformation of the way these agencies operate," said Jeff Ruch, executive director of PEER. "Ultimately it will lead to corporations taking over management of our resources altogether. They're proposing replacing career scientists with consultants who will be primarily motivated by getting the next contract renewed. So they are much less likely to report inconvenient findings back to management."

Diversity Suffers

To add insult to injury, not only are the park and forest service undergoing these cuts, but they are being forced to pay for the studies to determine whether certain jobs should be privatized out of their own already-strapped budgets. In a memo to the Assistant Secretary for Policy, Management and Budget, the National Park Service Director noted that the studies cost about $3,000 per job, for a total of $2.5 to $3 million to comply with Bush's mandate. The memo outlines how the source of these funds has not been identified, and how park services will need to be curtailed, during the busiest summer months to boot, in order to come up with the funds. The memo also explains that the privatization push will be a major blow to the park service's diversity, since a high proportion of the jobs being studied are filled by women or minorities.

"In recent years we have sought to increase the diversity of our agency workforce," says the memo. "These studies have the potential to impact this effort, for example 89 percent of the jobs proposed for study in the Washington D.C. area may affect the diversity of our workforce. Studies in San Francisco and Santa Fe show large concentrations of diverse [employees in jobs being studied] as well. This potential impact upon this workforce concerns us."

Compromising Safety

The privatization means that thousands of well-paying, mostly union jobs will be replaced by largely non-union private contractor positions. Critics of the plan also fear that as is often the case with privatization, it will mean a reduction in quality and thoroughness of services, as companies cut corners to maximize their profits and keep costs low to win bids for future contracts. For the park and forest service, this could mean less maintenance work done protecting fragile environments and the safety of parkgoers, and less effective fire-fighting and other crucial services.

In just one example of how privatization is expected to compromise safety across the spectrum of jobs, a June letter to Secretary of Commerce Donald Evans signed by a number of Congressmen points out how privatization of the federal seafood inspectors "would risk an increase in the incidence of serious illness, death or other problems from contaminated seafood or seafood that otherwise fails to meet inspection standards."

The Congressmen acknowledge the fact that private contractors would potentially compromise their performance in search of profit. "We would add that utilizing private sector firms for this vital inspection function would also at least raise the idea in the minds of some that the inspection contractors could certify questionable seafood shipments in order to maximize earnings," says the letter.

In a worst-case scenario, the privatization of park and forest service jobs will dovetail with the search for profit from national parks, whether through timber sales, increased tourism or the privatization of micro-organisms. The same or affiliated companies that are seeking to buy timber or explore and privatizate micro-organisms could also be hiring the park employees who theoretically oversee the protection of the environment.

"It's often true that companies that get contracts for environmental protection are related to companies that are polluting, so it's a conflict of interest," said

Brendan Danaher, a policy analyst for the AFGE. "We think if there's one thing that should remain under the public sector it's protecting the environment."

Ruch notes that under the new structure, "you could have Georgia Pacific National Forest—a park run by a timber company. There's no reason why Walt Disney couldn't bid on managing the Everglades national park."

Burrows fears the dual privatization of employees and micro-organisms could open the door to out of control prospecting, patenting and selling of micro-organisms (along with other forms of exploitation of resources) with little regard for bioethics or protection of these organisms and their often fragile environments.

Resistance Brewing

Between the unions, non-profit groups like PEER and various legislators, there is plenty of resistance to the federal employee privatization plan in general and the park and forest service privatization specifically. In June U.S. Rep. Nick Rahall (D-WV) in the House and Sen. Harry Reid (D-NV) in the Senate introduced the Park Professionals Protection Act, which would prevent the privatizing of park and forest service jobs.

"The livelihoods of the ambassadors to the national parks are at risk for the purpose of hiring individuals whose politics mirror the Bush administration's anti-conservation priorities," said Rahall, adding that it is a "bogus idea" to think out-sourced contractors could do a better job than career federal employees.

Reid said, "Our national parks were created to protect special places in nature as a legacy to future generations. They should be managed for posterity, not profit."

Burrows thinks that given the psychic and symbolic importance our ever-diminishing areas of natural wilderness and beauty have for the American people, not only are park and forest service employees and micro-organisms in danger, but our culture and way of life as a whole.

"These are our commons, the Grand Canyon and Yellowstone are the only two areas in the whole United States that people see as our common areas," she said. "If you don't have that as a common public area free from commercialization, what do you have left?"

Would you support a pesticide-spraying program in your community to combat the spread of West Nile virus?

The Bug Wars: West Nile Virus vs. Pesticide Poisoning: Four Years after West Nile Virus Was Found in New York City, It Continues to Spread. Are the Pesticides Used to Control the Virus Doing Us More Harm than Good?

Michelle Muelle

On Monday, July 24, 2000, by order of Mayor Rudolph Giuliani, New York City's Central Park was shut down. On that evening the park was sprayed with pesticides that would wipe out mosquitoes potentially infected with West Nile virus. While people in the city were concerned about being infected with the virus, not everybody was in agreement with the mayor on the use of pesticides. One environmental organization filed a lawsuit against the city because they felt the pesticides being used were hazardous to the public's health.

The debate over pesticides used to spray mosquitoes will continue to grow as West Nile virus continues to spread throughout the country.

A Virus on the Go

We have all been bitten at one time or another by a mosquito. They are annoying insects that feed on human and animal blood and can easily spread disease. St. Louis encephalitis, Eastern equine encephalitis, and West Nile virus are all mosquito-borne illnesses. West Nile virus was first discovered in Africa in 1937 and did not appear in the United States until it was found in New York City in 1999. In February 2003, the Centers for Disease Control and Prevention reported that West Nile virus could now be found in 44 states and has caused more than 300 deaths.

Children, teenagers, and adults under 50 who are infected by the virus often will not be affected. The biggest threat is to older people. They may develop high fever, body ache, disorientation, and paralysis or death in the most severe cases.

To Spray or Not to Spray

Spraying pesticides to destroy adult mosquitoes and their eggs is one method used to stop the spread of West Nile virus. There are many different types of pesticides used today for mosquito control. All pesticides are poisonous and dangerous if not used correctly. The body absorbs them by inhalation, ingestion, or skin penetration. High exposure can cause dizziness, headaches, fatigue, vomiting, and abdominal cramps. Some people are sensitive to even a low exposure of pesticide and will experience temporary eye and skin irritation. It also can irritate an existing condition such as asthma.

Weighing the health risks from pesticides against the chance of getting sick from West Nile virus can be difficult in some cases. Bob Peterson, a risk assessment scientist from Montana State University, says, "The risk associated with properly used pesticides is much lower than the risk associated with West Nile virus." Still it is up to your local officials and community leaders to decide if it is beneficial to spray in your area.

Washington, D.C., is one city that has chosen to limit the spraying of pesticides because they have a lot of people who have asthma. Spraying pesticides would put them at a greater risk.

Cities that do spray lower the risk of potential danger by informing the community when, where, and what type of pesticide they will be using. Spraying usually takes place very early in the morning or late at night when most people are sleeping.

Take Charge

Many people are still not convinced about the safety of pesticides and feel helpless when their community is being sprayed. If you are concerned about pesticide spraying in your area, the Environmental Protection Agency recommends families take these steps to protect themselves and minimize the risk:

- If possible, remain inside when spraying takes place.
- Close windows and doors before spraying begins.
- Cover outdoor furniture and toys or wash them with soap and water after spraying.
- Consult your doctor if you begin experiencing any symptoms from the pesticide spraying.
- Turn off your air conditioning before spraying begins.
- Wash exposed skin surfaces with soap and water if you come in contact with the pesticide.

Some communities are using other methods to fight against West Nile virus (see "Fight the Bite," at right). Knowing what is being done in your community and taking the proper precautions will minimize your chances of getting sick.

Fight the Bite

Spraying with pesticides is not the only way to fight mosquitoes. The New York State Department of Health started a "Fight the Bite" campaign to inform the public how they can prevent the spread of mosquitoes. Other states have similar programs. Here are some suggestions offered to citizens:

- Because mosquitoes breed in water, remove from your yard tin cans, old tires, plastic containers, ceramic pots, or anything that holds standing water.
- Drill holes in the bottoms of recycling containers.
- Turn over plastic pools.
- Change water in the bird bath.
- Make sure all windows and doors have screens.
- Wear a long-sleeved shirt, long pants, and socks and shoes if you are going to be outside for a long period of time during dusk or dawn.
- Always wear insect repellent that contains DEET. But make sure you follow all the directions when applying it.
- Encourage your neighbors and local businesses to reduce potential breeding sites as well.
- Organize a community-wide clean-up drive. For more information about how you can "Fight the Bite," contact the New York State Department of Health or your state or local health department.

For More Info

Centers for Disease Control and Prevention www.cdc.gov/ncidod/dvbid/westnile/index.htm Answers basic questions about prevention, reporting, and statistics, and provides links to state and local government Web sites.

Environmental Protection Agency www.epa.gov Click on "Pesticides" and "Human Health."

Objective

Students will be able to identify protective behaviors for minimizing the risk of mosquito bites that could transmit West Nile virus, and also the risk of exposure to dangerous levels of pesticides.

Review/Discuss

- Describe how pesticides enter the body and what effects they may have, including in sensitive people who can have problems with even low exposure to the pesticide. (The body can absorb the pesticide by inhalation, ingestion, or skin penetration. High exposure can cause dizziness, headaches, fatigue, vomiting, and abdominal cramps. Some very sensitive people can experience temporary eye and skin irritation, or flare-ups of existing conditions such as asthma.)
- What are some steps that a family can take to minimize the risk associated with the use of pesticides in their area? (In most communities the spraying takes place late at night or very early in the morning, when people are sleeping. Cover items

that family members will use, or wash them after the spraying is complete. Remain indoors when spraying is taking place. Turn off air conditioners and close windows and doors in advance. If you think you have come in contact with a pesticide, wash exposed skin surfaces and consult your doctor if you begin experiencing symptoms.)

Activities

1. Assign students to research and develop a coloring book, game, song, or other educational tool for elementary students, to convey the concepts and behaviors necessary to minimizing the risk of mosquito bites that could transmit West Nile virus. If you have cross-age teaching opportunities, the students from your classes may be able to earn credit for teaching these prevention strategies to younger kids.

2. Similarly, assign students to prepare another cross-age activity—this one for elders in your community—on identifying protective behaviors for minimizing the risk of exposure to dangerous levels of pesticides, when your community has made the decision to do preventive spraying. Be sure to discuss your goals in making the presentation to local resource personnel who have expertise in working with an elderly population.

Teacher Resources

- The New York State Department of Health has a variety of publications on West Nile virus available in PDF format on the Web, including a "Fight the Bite" brochure with tips for citizens on protecting yourself and your home. Go to www.health.state.ny.us/nysdoh/westnile/index.htm.
- The National Pesticide Information Center, a cooperative effort of Oregon State University and the Environmental Protection Agency, has a toll-free number—(800) 858-7378—and offers fact sheets on pesticides and a special page on West Nile virus (see http://npic.orst.edu).

Fact Sheet on West Nile Virus:
Why Spraying Pesticides Doesn't Eliminate Mosquitoes
Valerie Denney Communications

In many communities, mosquito abatement consists primarily of trucks spraying a pesticide designed to kill adult mosquitoes, a method called adulticiding. However, adulticiding is not effective because it kills only about 10 percent of adult mosquitoes.

It is difficult for trucks to spray between houses or walls, and many mosquitoes are simply out of reach of the spray. In addition, adulticiding does not affect mosquitoes in the egg, larva or pupa stages. New mosquitoes hatch to replace the adult mosquitoes killed by the spray within 12 to 16 days. According to the U.S. Environmental Protection Agency (EPA), effective mosquito prevention programs are conducted by "Eliminating breeding habitats or applying pesticides to control the early life stages of the mosquito. Prevention programs, such as elimination of any standing water that could serve as a breeding site, help reduce the adult mosquito population and the need to apply other pesticides for adult mosquito control."

Mosquitoes can also become resistant to the pesticide sprays after repeated exposures. As mosquitoes become resistant, increasingly toxic chemicals are used to eliminate them.

Pesticides can be harmful to human health and the environment.

Each pesticide has a different potential threat to human and environmental health. Many commonly used pesticides are toxic to the human nervous system and have been linked to cancer. Young children, as well as adults who suffer from respiratory problems such as asthma, are particularly vulnerable to pesticide exposure.

- Synthetic pyrethroids, such as resmethrin or permethrin (trade name 'BioMist') act on nerve cells by disrupting the transmission of impulses down the cell. They are toxic to fish and beneficial aquatic insects. Additionally, the inert ingredients in some pyrethroid formulations are known or suspected carcinogens. (Mueller-Beilschmidt, 1990)
- Organophosphates such as chlorpyrifos ('MosquitoMist' or 'Dursban') or malathion, are often used in truck spraying applications. Organophosphates are more toxic to vertebrates than other classes of insecticides. (George Ware, Professor Emeritus, Department of Entomology, University of Arizona). These compounds interfere with the breakdown of important enzymes of the nervous system (cholinesterase). Little is known about the neurological effects of long-term, low-dose, repeated exposure, but it may result in cumulative poisoning and affect neurodevelopment and growth in children (Eskenazi, Bradman and Castorina, 1999) At high doses, malathion, like other organophosphates, can over stimulate the nervous system causing nausea, dizziness or confusion. Severe

high-dose poisoning with any organophosphate can cause convulsions, respiratory paralysis and death. (U.S. E.P.A.)

- Altosid (active ingredient methoprene) is one commonly used product that works by preventing insects from developing into adults. Insect growth regulators are considered less hazardous than adulticides because they have selective action in insect growth. However, methoprene can harm beneficial insects, including those that prey on mosquitoes. (Montague, 1998)

Mosquito Management Two:
What Can Municipalities Do to Manage Mosquitoes?

Ecological methods are effective mosquito managers. An integrated pest management (IPM) program that includes monitoring for high mosquito populations and disease, community education and action to maximize natural controls and minimize breeding sites, and larvaciding (killing immature mosquitoes) when necessary, can control mosquitoes more effectively.

- Monitor mosquito populations by using traps and by checking ponds and sources of water for signs of mosquito larvae.
- Educate residents on ways to reduce mosquito breeding areas.
- Eliminate breeding areas by draining areas of stagnant water where possible and aerating ponds.
- Enhance drainage by keeping catch basins free of debris and flowing properly.
- Stock ornamental ponds with mosquito larvae-eating fish of the Gambusia genus. However, since these fish are not native to the Chicago area, they should only be stocked in enclosed water so they will remain in the area in need of control and not threaten the ecology of natural areas by competing with native species for food. (Beyond Pesticides/National Coalition Against the Misuse of Pesticides, 2002)
- Use larvacide as necessary to treat areas and water where mosquitoes breed such as catch basins and drainage ditches.
- Horticultural oils (vegetable based) are effective in killing larvae in water and sinking egg rafts on the surface. They also can kill beneficial organisms, including some mosquito predators. (Beyond Pesticides/National Coalition Against the Misuse of Pesticides, 2002)

Excerpt from 1991 Report of the Village President of Franklin Park, IL

The Village ceased aerial adulticiding 21 years ago. It was felt that chemical fogging from trucks was not only ineffective, it was adding toxic chemicals to the environment that could endanger the animal life including humans.

Alternative programs included larvaciding in catch basins and culverts using dormant or bacterial products. Also, residents were encouraged to attract birds to our community.

Results: Our bird population has steadily increased throughout the years since we stopped spraying. As for the mosquito populations, we have the same and often less of them than towns that have continued to adulticide.

Bonuses to our programs have been a great savings of tax money, an increase in bird and mosquito predator insects, and hopefully a safer environment for our animal life including our people.

—Jack B. Williams, former Village President, Franklin Park, IL

Mosquito Management Three:
You Can Manage Mosquitoes

A successful strategy for protecting yourself from mosquitoes includes two steps: eliminating breeding sites and avoiding mosquito bites.

Eliminate Breeding Sites:

- Mosquitoes don't travel far. Keep from breeding mosquitoes around your home by emptying containers with standing water. These may include: buckets, garbage cans and garbage can lids, swimming pool covers, children's toys, plant saucers, tarps and other places where water may collect.
- Fix dripping outdoor water faucets.
- Clean gutters regularly and change the water in bird baths and water barrels frequently.
- Drill holes at the bottom of recycling bins and other outdoor containers and turn them over so that they do not collect water.
- Get rid of unnecessary debris on your property, such as old tires.
- Stock ornamental, contained ponds with mosquito-eating fish. Many fish species, such as fathead minnows, guppies, goldfish, and golden shiners are good mosquito larvae predators.
- Use B.T.I. (Bacillus thuringiensis israeliensis) in ponds or other standing water on your property. B.T.I. is a strain of bacteria that kills mosquito and black fly larvae. B.T.I. disks are sold at hardware stores and lawn and garden centers under the name "Mosquito Dunks". The disks are considered a less hazardous pesticide because they target water-borne insects. However, B.T.I. can irritate the skin and eyes and affect those with weak immune systems.

Avoid Mosquito Bites:

- Use citronella candles at outdoor gatherings. These candles only control mosquitoes in the immediate vicinity when there is no wind.
- Set up carbon dioxide traps ('Mosquito Magnets'). These traps send out carbon dioxide to attract mosquitoes which are then vacuumed in and killed.

Would you support a pesticide-spraying program in your community to combat the spread of West Nile virus?

- Encourage birds and bats in your yard. A mouse-eared bat can consume 600 mosquitoes in one hour. (League of Women Voters, 1996)
- Keep mosquitoes out of your home by making sure screens and weather stripping are intact.
- Use yellow, non-attractive light bulbs at the entrances of your home.
- Apply natural repellants such as vinegar, the oils of citronella, eucalyptus, garlic or peppermint. Bite Blocker for Kids, a repellant made with soybean oil, was found to be somewhat effective against mosquitoes according to a study by Fradin and Day published in the New England Journal of Medicine in July 2002.
- Where protective or light-colored clothing when outdoors in the early morning and at dusk. Mosquitoes are more attracted to dark colors.

Resources

Established in 1994, the Safer Pest Control Project (SPCP) addresses both the public health risks and environmental impacts of pesticide use and advocates for safer alternatives, such as integrated pest management (IPM) in schools and day care centers, housing, yards and parks and agriculture. SPCP provides common sense pest management assistance and consulting services to communities and organizations, service providers and government agencies, housing managers and others. For more information, visit www.spcpweb.org.

National Pesticide Information Center, www.npic.orst.edu

U. S. Environmental Protection Agency, www.epa.gov

Beyond Pesticides, www.beyondpesticides.org

Centers for Disease Control and Prevention, www.cdc.org

Citigroup Looks at Recycled Paper Use

Jim Johnson

A well-known financial services company is looking at ways to cut back on its use of copy paper and increase the recycled content of the paper that it does use.

Citigroup is teaming with the Alliance for Environmental Innovation, a project of Environmental Defense, to help reduce the environmental impact of copy paper use. ``The myth of the `paperless office' is just that. Even with a move towards paperless technologies, the amount of copy paper used continues to increase dramatically, causing significant environmental impacts," said Jackie Cefola, project manager of the alliance.

A team including employees from both Citigroup and the alliance will tackle the project. Citigroup employees will represent areas such as business services, purchasing, marketing and environmental affairs.

The alliance, at this point, is working with Citigroup to test the suitability of recycled content paper and to influence the overall amount of paper being used.

That effort includes employee education programs along with a push to use both sides of sheets of paper when making copies, Cefola said. The trial effort is taking place in Citigroup's New York City offices where the company employs about 25,000, and Cefola hopes to have results compiled this year. The initial project will measure reductions in energy and resource use, solid waste and pollution.

"Our company is strongly committed to helping preserve the environment for future generations, and we look forward to having our employees become actively involved in finding ways to create environmentally beneficial results when producing and using copy paper," said Citigroup's Pamela P. Flaherty, senior vice president for global community relations.

The alliance and Citigroup started testing 30 percent postconsumer recycled copy paper in April and began a second round of testing in June.

If the testing goes well, Citigroup will recommend that all of the bank's U.S. operations use postconsumer recycled copy paper. "We're focusing on New York operations right now," Cefola said.

Issues deterring the overall use of recycled-content paper revolved around quality, availability and pricing, she said.

Government testing shows there is virtually no quality difference between virgin paper and paper containing 30 percent recycled content these days, she said.

Availability, also once an issue, is no longer a problem, Cefola said. Some companies see price parity between virgin and recycled-content paper while others either can secure a price discount or pay a premium for recycled-content, Cefola said.

Citigroup operates under a variety of brand names, including Citibank, Salomon Smith Barney, Travelers, Primerica and CitiFinancial. Citigroup and its subsidiaries employ about 145,000 in the United States and another 123,000 outside the country.

Contact *Waste News* reporter Jim Johnson at (330) 865-6171 or jpjohnson@ crain.com

Eugene, Ore., Company Uses Forest-Friendly Techniques to Make Recycled Paper

Joe Harwood

Mar. 25—Carolyn Moran's Living Tree Paper Co. lives up to its name.

The tiny Eugene-based firm is on the cutting edge of forest-friendly paper making: Instead of using virgin wood pulp to make its printing, writing and specialty papers, Living Tree mixes imported industrial hemp and flax fibers with recycled office paper.

The result is a tree-free, chlorine-free product virtually identical in appearance and quality to standard white office paper.

"We don't use any new trees to make it," said Moran, the company's CEO. "And we don't use chlorine to make it white."

While use of recycled paper has soared in recent years, only a small handful of companies in the nation make and sell paper that contains industrial hemp.

Moran, who has a background in environmental activism, founded the company in 1994 with the aim of producing a "nonwood" paper that didn't require the denuding of forests and the use of caustic chemicals to turn wood chips into the opaque, soupy pulp that is dried and rolled into paper.

"The whole concept is to save trees," Moran said.

After struggling for several years to sell its products on a large scale, Living Tree now is on the verge of a breakthrough. Within the next four or five weeks, the company's printer and copier paper will appear on the shelves of the roughly 1,100 Staples Inc. office supply stores across the United States. The new product is part of Staples' push to expand its environmentally friendly offerings, a spokesman said.

"This is huge for us," Moran said.

Whether consumers respond is the big question. A ream of Living Tree printer paper retails for $6.99, compared to about $5 or less for similar paper that contains virgin wood.

Moran is hoping that a growing number of customers will pay that premium.

With Staples selling its paper, Living Tree is projecting sales of $3 million to $5 million for the fiscal year starting April 1. That should help the company turn a profit. At its current sales level of about $2 million a year, the company is just breaking even, Moran said.

Living Tree has been growing steadily since its inception, gradually winning big corporate clients such as Nike, manufacturing conglomerate Mitsubishi and outdoor clothing manufacturer Patagonia. These corporate customers are willing to pay extra for environmentally correct paper.

But convincing retail chains such as Staples, Office Depot and Office Max proved difficult. "It is incredible for us to get into Staples," Moran said. "We had to be very persistent." The retail chains don't like the price difference, Moran said.

"They think the consumer wants cheap paper at the expense of the environment," she said. "But that is not the case."

Tom Nutile, a spokesman for Massachusetts-based Staples, said the company for years has stocked recycled items as part of its commitment to the environment. A year ago, the company conducted a study of its products and found about 400 items with recycled content, he said.

"Since then, we've been trying to increase the percentage of those products in our stores," Nutile said. "It's the right thing to do."

Staples decided to sell Living Tree's printer paper because "it's high quality, darn good paper," he said.

Moran said the 24-pound printer paper Staples will offer is 90 percent recycled office paper and 10 percent hemp-flax fiber. The hemp-flax content gives the paper its strength.

"We get one shot at this," Moran said. "If it moves off the shelves, maybe Office Depot and others will realize it's a hot product that consumers want."

Staples plans to sell a ream (500 sheets) of the paper for $6.99, about $2 more than comparable, wood-fiber brands. Moran contends that if consumers know the paper is available, they will seek it out.

The paper carries a "green premium" largely because so few mills are equipped to produce it and so little of it is made. It's the same principle that makes organically grown food more expensive than conventionally grown food—although organic prices have dropped as production has increased due to skyrocketing consumer demand.

Only a tiny faction of mills have the facilities to turn industrial hemp, flax, kenaf and other nonwood fibers into pulp. Pulp and paper mills the world over are almost exclusively geared to convert wood into pulp and then paper. Though the pulping processes are similar, flax or hemp (with their longer fibers) cannot be fed into a pulp mill that is set up to use virgin wood fiber. Economies of scale

Since the 19th century, the bulk of technological innovation—and capital spending—in paper making has been focused on wood pulp. Forests were plentiful, wood was cheap, and people didn't worry about clear-cutting.

The abundant wood supply coupled with economies of scale means industry stalwarts such as International Paper Co. and Georgia Pacific Co. can provide consumers a ream of fine white paper for $3 or $4.

That's left a small handful of niche mills to do nonwood pulping for items ranging from tea bags and cotton paper to currency.

Moran insists that as nonwood papers become more popular, more mills will step into the niche and the price will drop.

"If people pay a couple of dollars more for it, maybe they'll use less," she said. "If people can't pay $2 more for this, I think we're all in trouble."

Moran essentially stumbled into the "nonwood" paper-making business. In 1989, she launched "Talking Leaves," a widely distributed pro-environmental magazine that promotes sustainability.

In 1993, Moran said she started searching for a tree-free paper on which to publish Talking Leaves. After studying her few available options, Moran received a grant to import paper made in China of industrial hemp and flax. The quality was poor and the paper wreaked havoc with printing presses, so Moran traveled to Eastern Europe and Russia looking for a better nonwood paper.

She eventually met up with Frank Riccio, co-founder of Danforth International Trade Associates, a supplier of specialty fibers and pulps made from nonwoods including industrial hemp, flax, kenaf and the like. Riccio, an expert in nonwood specialty pulping processes, encouraged Moran to start her own paper company and offered her technical assistance.

She founded Living Tree in 1994, and by late 1995 she was selling her first nonwood paper products. Finding a partner

In 1996, Moran invited Harry Bondareff aboard as a partner. Bondareff, with a background in business and finance, had recently earned a master's degree in environmental studies from the University of Oregon. Bondareff, now based in Portland, serves as the company's vice president and national sales manager.

In the ensuing years, Moran and Bondareff have developed partnerships with small pulp and paper mills in Massachusetts, Maine and Toronto, Canada, which make the specialty paper for Living Tree.

Because industrial hemp and flax pulp is not readily available in the United States, the company imports the pulp from France and Spain, where industrial hemp and flax is grown in fields as an annual crop.

Before shipment to the United States, the hemp and flax pulp is pressed into sheets and dried. Once it arrives at the mills, it is rehydrated and mixed with pulp made from recycled office paper.

The United States outlawed the production of industrial hemp in the 1930s amid the scare over marijuana use, despite that fact that industrial hemp contains only insignificant amounts of the psychoactive chemical that gives marijuana smokers their high.

Industrial hemp and marijuana look much the same, but industrial hemp is useless as a drug.

Industrial hemp production is legal in numerous countries, including Canada.

Having to import the industrial hemp from Europe adds costs, Moran said. Recent actions by the U.S. Drug Enforcement Administration to restrict products containing industrial hemp could affect Living Tree's use of hemp as a fiber source.

"I'm not dependent on it, but I'd like to continue using it because its long fibers really add strength to the paper," she said.

Thus far, however, the DEA has only targeted consumer products such as cosmetics or foods that contain industrial hemp.

Moran said there needs to be more research and development of alternative fiber sources for paper making, such as straw, to move the paper industry away from using trees.

"There's plenty of straw here in the Northwest. It's an agricultural by-product," she said. "We just don't have any pulping facilities for straw right now, but I think it's going to happen in the next three to five years."

In the meantime, Moran said she will continue to spread the word about the ecological benefits of nonwood paper.

"Consumers have to play a vital role in reshaping the pulp and paper industry," she said. "Consumers have to let the industry know they want tree-free paper."

Living Tree Paper Co.

- Business: Produces tree-free paper made from flax, hemp pulp and recycled paper pulp
- Owners: Carolyn Moran and Harry Bondareff
- Employees: 5
- Annual sales: About $2 million
- Founded: 1994 in Eugene

Living Tree's Steps to Making Tree-Free Paper

1. Contracts with mills in Massachusetts, Maine and Toronto to make the paper.
2. Imports hemp and flax pulp from France and Spain.
3. Pulp arrives as dried sheets at the mills. There, water is added to sheets and they are mixed with postconsumer paper waste (recycled paper), then pressed to form Living Tree's paper products.
4. From the mills, the paper is shipped directly to customers, to distributors or to Living Tree warehouses in Eugene and New Jersey.

To see more of *The Register-Guard*, Eugene, Ore., or to subscribe to the newspaper, go to http://www.registerguard.com

TICKER SYMBOL(S): SPLS, ODP, OMX, IP, GP

Safety Precautions for Summer Training

Ken Mannie

The Summer of 2001 witnessed several devastating training and practice-related deaths at just about every level of play. Each incident had its own set of special circumstances, but the heat and/or humidity was at least partly culpable in each case.

As coaches, we were frustrated and haunted by questions and second-guessing. What, if anything, could have been done to prevent these tragedies? Even with all of the scientific information available, there were no clearcut answers. But we were obligated to continue our search for every piece of wisdom we could unearth for the safety of the athletes on our watch.

As we enter the summer of 2002, let us review the basic physiological stresses induced by a hot environment and how the body responds and adapts to them. And, more importantly, let us zero in on the safety precautions that coaches have to take.

Adapting to the Heat

Research has taught us that summer conditioning procedures are necessary for heat acclimatization and that the training must be gradual, progressive, and prudently executed, with detailed attention to the environmental conditions.

Acclimatization is a process involving both physical and psychological adaptations to a new or changing environment. It may be a move from a cooler to warmer climate, or simply an adjustment from the mild temperatures of spring to the hot and humid conditions of summer.

Following is an over-simplified explanation of the body's adjustment to external heat during exercise: The cardiovascular system (CVS) will compensate for the heat by shunting blood to the skin. This will improve the body's ability to cool itself by dissipating internal heat, but will diminish the blood supply to the working muscles.

If the air temperature is mildly warm, the body can release a portion of the internal heat overload through sweat evaporation. But when high humidity is coupled with warm air temperatures, it doubles the body's thermal stress and may stifle the body's ability to evaporate the sweat and cool itself.

This "Catch 22" happenstance will force the CVS to meet the competing demands of the thermoregulatory system and the requirements of muscle metabolism.

This physiological dilemma will be exacerbated whenever hydration is inadequate and/or the activity is prolonged, resulting in a convolution of heat-related problems.

Acclimatization can reduce the risks. The process encompasses approximately 10–14 short, less intense training sessions in the warmer environment. The initial duration of these workouts should be between 20–30 minutes at a low to moderate intensity level, with liberal fluid breaks.

There should also be a gradual build-up in the frequency of the sessions. Our football training, for example, starts with two days per week from mid-May through mid-June and progresses to 3–4 days per week from mid-June through July.

Areas that have extremely hot and humid climates would be wise to hold the initial workout sessions during a milder part of the day (early morning/early evening). This will produce a gradual acclimatization to the variable conditions throughout the day.

Heat acclimatization offers the following physiological benefits:

1. Reduction in heart rate.
2. Reduction in core temperature.
3. Increase in the cutaneous (skin) blood flow and perspiration rate that facilitate the cooling process.
4. Earlier beginning of perspiration, thus expediting the cooling process.
5. Decrease in the loss of vital electrolytes (minerals such as potassium and sodium).

To summarize: The gradual, systematic, and progressive steps in the acclimatization process will eventually produce well-conditioned athletes with a much higher heat tolerance than their sedentary counterparts or zealots who rush blindly into summer conditioning drills.

Wet Bulb Globe Temperature

Our sports medicine staff uses a "sling psychrometer," a hand-held instrument that measures the heat stress index before every scheduled workout or practice. The heat stress index is calculated by a Wet Bulb Globe Temperature (WBGT), which takes into account the air temperature, relative humidity, and solar radiation.

It is very important to know the relative humidity, which is a measure of how much moisture the air contains, since it affects the amount of heat that can be lost through the evaporation of heat. A hot and humid day that is compounded with limited air movement severely hampers the body's ability to cool itself through convection.

The WBGT index is a practical measurement for assessing potentially harmful environmental conditions. The readings are gauged into low, moderate, high, and hazardous risk categories, providing the sports medicine and coaching staffs with solid information that will help them make prudent decisions on the duration and intensity of the workout/practice.

If the reading gauges a "high" or "hazardous" risk, the activity may be re-scheduled for a safer time or day.

We recommend that at least two of your staff members learn how to take the WBGT by using the sling psychrometer prior to all summer workouts and practices.

Identifying Heat-Related Stresses

Two heat-related stresses of paramount concern are heat exhaustion and heat stroke. Coaches must be aware of the symptoms and immediate care procedures for each problem.

Heat exhaustion, while rarely a life-threatening condition, can lead to more serious problems if left unattended. The symptoms of heat exhaustion can include headache, nausea, dizziness, light-headedness, rapid pulse, and muscle cramps.

An athlete with any of these symptoms should be required to stop the activity, be taken to a cool, shady area, and told to sit or lie down in a supine (with slightly elevated feet) position. Cool liquids (water or a sports drink) can then be given to sip on. Activity should not be resumed until all of the symptoms have passed and qualified medical clearance has been granted.

Coaches must understand that heat exhaustion, when left untreated, can lead to heat stroke—a significantly more dangerous condition.

The symptoms of heat stroke can vary, but may include any or all of the following: disorientation, an extremely high body temperature (above 103 degrees Fahrenheit orally), red, hot, dry skin, rapid, strong pulse, nausea and/or vomiting, throbbing headache, and unconsciousness.

If any of these warning signs are detected, you must understand that you are dealing with a potentially life-threatening emergency requiring medical assistance.

Do the following immediately:

- Call 911 for emergency assistance, or the closest, most readily available medical staff in your situation.
- Get the victim to an air-conditioned or cool, shady area.
- Cool the victim with any available means; water hose, shower, wet towels, farming, etc.
- If severe nausea and vomiting are apparent, do not administer fluids. Make sure that the airway is clear if the individual is unconscious.
- If possible, monitor body temperature until it drops below 101 degrees Fahrenheit.

Hydration

It is vitally important to incorporate and maintain a sound hydration strategy for workouts, practices, and games. Unfortunately, an athlete's thirst mechanism is a poor indicator of actual fluid needs.

During exercise, athletes should start drinking cool (50–59 degrees F.) fluids at a rate of at least 8 ounces every 15–20 minutes. Water is fine, but for intense activities lasting longer than one hour, the sports carbohydrate/electrolyte drinks may be a better choice. Reason: They provide needed energy and mineral replacement, as well as fluid replacement. The palatability of these drinks also encourages a higher usage, which helps in meeting the objectives.

Fruit juices and soft drinks that have a 12% or higher carbohydrate concentration are not good choices during exercise, as they may cause gastrointestinal distress. Fruit juices are fine for post-exercise recovery, and it might be a good idea to avoid all carbonated, caffeinated soft drinks.

Pre-hydration is a critical component in this strategy Athletes should drink the appropriate beverages liberally throughout the day and evening, and should be encouraged to take a plastic water bottle to meetings, class, etc., and to drink from them regularly.

Approximately two hours prior to an intense workout or competition, the athlete should gradually ingest at least 17–18 ounces of fluid.

Post-exercise/competition hydration calls for at least 20–24 ounces of fluid for every pound of body weight lost (which is primarily fluid loss).

Athletes should be taught to monitor their urine for signs of dehydration. Dark yellow urine and little or no urine over the course of several hours can be indicators of dehydration. Ideally, athletes should urinate every couple of hours and it should be relatively clear in color.

Final Rep

Further suggestions for preventing heat-related problems:

- Perform warm-up activities in the shade whenever possible to prevent sudden excessive rises in body temperature.
- Wear loose-fitting, light-colored clothing when possible.
- Adjust the intensity and/or the duration of the workout session in accordance with the environmental conditions and the conditioning level of the athletics.
- Be aware of the "perceived exertion" or the outward distress indicators that the athletes may be telegraphing via their body language. Their inability to produce the desired effort can be a precursor to heat stress.

Exercise-Induced Asthma

Exercise-induced asthma (ETA) affects approximately 15% of the general population. Its symptoms range from coughing, wheezing, chest tightness, shortness of breath, and fatigue to prolonged recovery times after exercise.

Asthma is an obstructive disease of the airways that is categorized by inflammation, bronchial wall edema (swelling), and mucus production. ETA is airway obstruction brought on by the combination of exercise and numerous environmental conditions (e.g., temperature, allergens, pollutants, etc.)

It is important to recognize the potential symptoms of this condition for medical referral. With proper treatment and precautionary measures in place, EIA can be effectively controlled and managed.

SEND YOUR QUESTIONS TO: Ken Mannie, Michigan State University, Duffy Daugherty Building, East Lansing, Ml 48824
(517) 355-7514
mannie@msu.edu

Heat Can Kill—Guidelines to Prevent Heat Illness in Athletics and Physical Education

Nita Unruh; Scott Unruh; Ed Scantling

In the wake of several publicized, tragic events that occurred during preseason training in both college and professional football, administrators, coaches, and physical educators must take time to re-evaluate how conditioning activities, daily practices, and classes are conducted during extreme heat. Administrators, coaches, and physical educators need to think in terms of legal liability and risk management when addressing this issue and to ask themselves how they can prevent such tragedies.

In football alone, 100 high school and college athletes have died from heat stroke since 1960 (Mueller & Diehl, 2001). Even worse, the per-year average is increasing, with 20 deaths in the past seven years and three deaths in 2001 (Mueller and Diehl, 2001). The issue was brought to the public's attention by the death of Korey Stringer, from the Minnesota Vikings; freshman football player Eraste Autin, at the University of Florida; and, in a less publicized case, Travis Stowers of Clinton High School in Indiana (DiRocco, 2001; Pucin, 2001). Could any of these tragedies have been prevented? This is a question the administrators at each of these institutions will be asking themselves for years to come. Is it possible that in this age of modern medicine we are still unable to prevent such catastrophic incidents in our elite athletes and our physical education classes? Could this same type of catastrophe happen in physical education classes that take place in extreme heat where we are teaching activities such as football and softball or doing fitness testing? Can administrators, coaches, and physical educators be held responsible for such deaths?

The answer to these questions is an overwhelming yes. The courts have held that coaches and administrators have been negligent in their duty to protect athletes from such incidents. In *Roventini v. Pasadena School* (1997), a court found coaches, athletic trainers, and administrators were all liable for the death of a student athlete. In this case, a 16-year-old football player died from heat exhaustion and dehydration after the first day of football practice. The legal question in this case was whether the coaches, athletic trainers, and administration were negligent in depriving the athlete of bodily integrity by denying him water and running him excessively in conditioning drills. Institutions have questioned whether they have a duty to student athletes in voluntary practices. In *Kleinknecht v. Gettysburg College, et al.* (1993), the courts established that an institution has a duty to respond quickly and provide adequate medical services to student athletes even if the activity performed by the athlete is voluntary. In the Kleinknecht case, a student athlete was participating in a voluntary preseason practice and collapsed from heat exhaustion. The absence of medical personnel (i.e., athletic trainers) on the field was deemed negligent. In Phoenix, Arizona, as well, coaches and administrators have been held

Nita Unruh, Scott Unruh, Ed Scantling, "Heat Can Kill—Guidelines to Prevent Heat Illness in Athletics and Physical Education." in *JOPERD—The Journal of Physical Education, Recreation & Dance*, vol. 73, no i6, p. 36(4), August 2002. Copyright © 2002 by American Alliance for Health, Physical Education, Recreation and Dance (AAHPERD). All rights reserved. Reproduced by permission.

negligent in their actions and decisions concerning student athletes and conditioning workouts (Cobb, 1992). Based on these cases and numerous others, there should be a demand for administrative policies and procedures that address the predisposition of an athlete or student to potentially life-threatening conditions related to heat exposure. Even though these legal examples pertain to athletics, the same conditions are evident in physical education classes.

In physical education classes, where participation is mandatory, teachers have a special legal duty to protect students from harm (Keeton, Dobbs, Keeton, & Owen, 1984). This is what is called a "special relationship," and with this special relationship it is the duty of the physical education teacher (as well as any other school employee) to take reasonable precautions to exercise control over the conduct of the student. (Keeton et al, 1984). This was evident in *Brahatcek v. Millard School* (1979), where a child died from an injury suffered when a golf club hit him in the head during a physical education class. The teacher and the school were found liable because inadequate supervision was provided during the activity. Even though this case and others did not involve heat illness, they all led to a judgment for the plaintiff based on the special relationship of supervising the student in all activities. In physical education that involves intense exercise, the heat produced by the body is 15 to 20 times above normal; the instructor should also consider the effect of the heat index on the body (Clark, 1998). With this in mind, physical educators should exercise control over what activities are performed in extreme heat.

What protocols should administrators, coaches, and physical educators consider when looking to create administrative policies and procedures to prevent death related to heat illness? Five guidelines come to mind when considering athletics. First, require that practice times be scheduled based upon recorded heat indexes (early morning or late evening). Second, provide strict monitoring of pre- and post-practice weight charts, and give complete and total responsibility to athletic trainers or team physicians for making the decision on when to return to, or continue with, practices. Third, ensure that if a student athlete demonstrates any symptoms of heat illness, they are not required to practice or continue practicing. Fourth, require coaches to permit water at all times during practice or provide frequent water breaks. Finally, require a limit on practice or on any intense drilling/conditioning segment of practice during times of extreme heat.

Most of these guidelines for athletics can be adapted for use with physical education classes. For example, physical educators could perhaps schedule less strenuous sport activities during early fall or late spring when the weather is warmer. Second, monitor the students closely as they participate in activities on warm weather days. Third, require that participation be restricted if a physical education student demonstrates any symptoms of heat illness. Fourth, require physical educators to permit water at all times during class and provide frequent water breaks. In fact, the physical educator may want to encourage students to bring water bottles to class. Finally, require a limit on the intense exercise segment of class during times of extreme heat. Table 1 summarizes these guidelines.

In addition to these guidelines, appropriate medical staff (i.e., athletic trainers) should be on site for all athletic practices and workouts, whether they are mandatory or voluntary. For physical education classes, the instructor should hold current CPR and first-aid certifications. These are not new ideas; in fact, some of these suggestions have been a part of the training programs established by the American College for Sport Medicine for years.

There is legal support for these guidelines, as well—first, it will protect the participant from undue risk, thus protecting the coaches, administrators, and physical educators from liability; second, it places risk decisions in the hands of qualified professionals, not in the hands of teachers, coaches, and athletes; third, it will absolve from liability those individuals who are not qualified to make such decisions.

One thing is clear, workouts and classes during extreme heat need to be modified and closely monitored. Personnel who are going to be supervising training sessions or physical education classes need to check the heat index before the activity begins, to see whether adjustments need to be made to workout schedules or class activities. Staff can measure the heat index in a variety of ways, one of which is to get a wet-bulb temperature—a measurement of the water vapor in the air ("Understanding Humidity," 2001). To get this measurement, you could use a thermometer and wrap the bulb in wet cotton, then sweep the bulb of the thermometer back and forth until the temperature stops dropping (Space, Telecommunications, and Radioscience Laboratory, 2002). A wet bulb temperature higher than 75 degrees Fahrenheit, warm-weather humidity above 90 percent, and temperatures above 82 degrees Fahrenheit all suggest that extreme caution should be undertaken (National Collegiate Athletic Association, 2001). Table 2 shows the approximate degree of hazard for various temperature ranges.

Adjustments to workouts or classes could include changing the time or content of the class or practice. Changing the time of a class may be impossible, but changing the activity is always possible. In extreme heat, coaches and teachers should also encourage acclimation to the weather conditions, monitor pre- and post-weight for athletes, and ensure good hydration. To acclimate an athlete or student, the coach or physical educator should start by exposing the participant to the condition for 10 minutes on the first day, and increase exposure daily. In addition, athletes should weigh-in before and after each practice, and players should be no less than two percent below the starting weight of their previous day's practice. Finally, practice or class should stop every 15 minutes for hydration.

Other procedural steps that could be taken include an education program for the staff and the participants. Participants, teachers, and all coaches need to know that water is life and that thirst is not an accurate measure of a body's need for water. Participants should drink water before and after practice or class as well as during activity. What a participant wears to a workout should also be discussed when educating staff and participants. Wearing light-colored clothing decreases the body's absorption of solar radiation. Protective gear and excessive tape restrict the sweat evaporation and other pathways for heat loss. Rubberized suits should never be worn to a workout. In addition to these simple lessons, staff need to be able to identify students and athletes who might have a predisposition to heatstroke. Some cues to this are body size and fat, aerobic status, acclimatization, and the individual's level of fitness (ACSM, 1985). Staff should also look for those students and athletes who inadequately rehydrate themselves during activity, those who regularly push themselves to capacity and beyond, and those who might be taking substances that are a diuretic or a stimulant (these could be over-the-counter drugs or nutritional supplements).

Coaches, physical educators, and participants also need to learn to recognize the symptoms of heat illness (table 3) and not dismiss them as signs of a bad day in class or on the practice field. If one or more of these symptoms is noticed, the student or athlete should cease activity and undertake cooling (e.g., by hydrating or getting out of the sun).

Prevention of heat illness or death from heat stroke requires administrators, coaches, and physical educators to take proactive measures to ensure that participants are protected. Administrative planning, such as having the appropriate staff on hand to monitor the heat index and practice sessions, is a good start. It is also extremely important to educate the coaches, physical educators, and student athletes on the causes and the prevention of heat illness and heat stroke. Implementing an education program and administrative procedures to ensure that all precautions are being taken is just the beginning. Once the process is in place, it is still up to the administrator to monitor the process and adjust it, if necessary, as well as to document any problems that occur. By following these simple guidelines, physical educators, coaches, and administrators might be able to protect themselves from a serious liability issue and, more important, prevent the loss of life.

Table 1: Suggestions for Preventing Heat Illness

Physical Education	*Athletics*
1. Consider scheduling intense activities for late fall through early spring.	1. Schedule practice according to the heat index.
2. Monitor students closely for signs of heat illness.	2. Monitor pre- and post-practice weight of participants.
3. If signs of heat illness appear, restrict activity.	3. If signs of heat illness appear, restrict activity.
4. Permit water at all times.	4. Permit water at all times.
5. Limit intense exercise segments during warm weather.	5. Limit intense drilling/ conditioning during extreme heat.

Table 2: Heat Illness Range Chart

Degrees in Fahrenheit	Hazard
Less than 64	Low
64–73	Moderate
73–82	High
Greater than 82	Hazardous

Table 3: Symptoms of Heat Illness

- Reduced perspiration
- Cramping
- Weakness
- Flushed skin
- Throbbing head
- Nausea
- Blurred vision
- Unsteadiness
- Incoherency

References

American College of Sports Medicine (1985). *Position stand: The prevention of thermal injuries during distance running.* Indianapolis, IN: Author.

Brahatcek v. Millard School District, 202 Neb. 86, 273 N.W.2d 680 (1979).

Clark, T. (1998). The hot zone. *Runners World*, 33(6), 70–76.

Cobb, C. (1992, October 3). Common' sense, education keys to athletes' safety. *The Phoenix Gazette.*

DiRocco, M. (2001, July 26). Florida freshman football player dies, Autin collapsed after workout last week. *The Florida Times-Union* (Jacksonville, FL), p. Cl.

Keeton, W. P., Dobbs, D. B., Keeton, R. E., & Owen, D. G. (1984). Limited Duty. In W. L. Prosser (Ed.), *Prosser and Keeton on the Law of Torts* (5th ed.; pp. 383–385). St. Paul, MN: West Publishing.

Kleinknecht v. Gettysburg College, et al., 989 F.2d 1360 (U.S. App., 3d Cir. 1993).

Mueller, F.O., & Diehl, J. L. (2001). *Annual survey of football injury research 19312001.* Chapel Hill, NC: National Center for Catastrophic Injury Research.

National Collegiate Athletic Association (2001). NCAA guideline 2c: Prevention of heat illness. In J. Painter (Ed.), *2001–2002 sports medicine handbook* (pp. 22–24). Indianapolis, IN: NCAA.

Pucin, D., (2001, Aug 14). Football tragedies; Silence falls preps death. *Los Angeles Times* (Home Edition), p. 1.

Roventini v. Pasadena Independent School District, 981 F. Supp. 1013 (1997); 1997 U.S. Dist. LEXIS 18805.

Space, Telecommunications, and Radio-science Laboratory. (2002). Humidity [On-line]. Available: http://www-star.stanford.edu/projects/mod-old/adhumid.html.

Understanding humidity. (2001, December 17). USA Today [On-line]. Available: http://www.usatoday.com/weather/whumdef.htm.

Nita Unruh (unruhnc@unk.edu) is an assistant professor, Scott Unruh (unruhs@unk.edu) is an assistant professor and athletic training education director, and Ed Scantling (scantlinge@unk.edu) is a chair and professor in the Department of HPERLS at the University of Nebraska Kearney, Kearney, NE 68849.

Water Fights

Alex Markels

The blizzards that dumped 8-plus feet of snow on Colorado in March and April were too little, too late for Ron Aschermann, a fourth-generation farmer in southeast Colorado's parched Arkansas Valley. After four years of drought, he and scores of other area farmers had already given up on planting this spring. For the moment, he says, "there's water to start a crop." The Rocky Ford Ditch, an irrigation canal in which he shares the water rights with 51 other farmers, is brimming with mountain runoff. Yet Aschermann fears a repeat of last summer, when the ditch ran dry in July and farmers went six weeks without a drop. "The crops just burned up," he says.

So Aschermann and his fellow shareholders in the ditch are packing it in. Rather than endure another year trying to coax onions and alfalfa from the bone-dry earth, they have decided to sell their water rights for $19 million to the thirsty Denver suburb of Aurora. The controversial transfer, now under review by a state district court judge, would reduce the already-beleaguered valley's farm production by about 2,600 acres. Diverted 160 miles north to fast-growing Aurora, the water would be enough to supply about 12,000 households during what could be another scorching summer.

Shriveled. Although spring storms have caused flooding in parts of the Midwest and replenished some eastern reservoirs, much of the West remains gripped by drought. Despite late-season snows, reservoirs in cities like Aurora remain less than one-third full, and even average precipitation won't refill them for three years or more. Unfortunately, National Weather Service forecasters now predict a return to dry weather in much of the region, all but guaranteeing more of the water shortages that have already cost residents from Colorado to California billions of dollars in water bills and shriveled vegetation.

While some climatologists blame global warming for the drought's severity, such episodes are hardly a new phenomenon. Studies of ancient tree rings suggest that dry spells have plagued the West for centuries. A megadrought about 700 years ago may have contributed to the disappearance of the Anasazi Indians, the region's first known human settlers. And three droughts over the past century—including the one in the 1930s that spawned the Dust Bowl—devastated agricultural life across the West, driving out homesteaders and shuttering towns.

This time around, however, it is not just farmers and ranchers who are hard pressed for water. Now the agrarian Old West must compete with the New West's burgeoning suburbs and even with endangered species that depend on ample stream flows. "The drought is a warning signal," says Gail Norton, secretary of the U.S. Department of Interior, which last week released a map highlighting western communities likely to experience water-supply crises over the next two decades. "Water shortages will be repeated even in average rainfall years because there's simply not enough supply to satisfy all the growing demands."

Until recently, Westerners could avoid this looming problem. Lulled by nearly two decades of above-average precipitation that preceded the current drought, cities like Aurora failed to acquire the water supplies needed to keep pace with their booming populations. Meanwhile, residents—millions of whom migrated from the East in recent decades—have landscaped homes and businesses as if they still lived in wetter climes, carpeting thousands of square miles with bluegrass lawns and other thirsty vegetation.

Even less frugal are many western farmers, whose crops consume about 90 percent of the region's water supply. Blessed by their forefathers with first dibs on cheap water subsidized, in part, by huge federal water projects, most have had little incentive to install water-saving technologies, such as drip irrigation systems. In recent years, total cultivated western acres have actually increased, further squeezing water supplies.

Conservationists, too, are demanding a share of the West's water supply. From New Mexico to Oregon, a slew of enviro-backed lawsuits are forcing farmers and developers to surrender some of the water they've nabbed to the needs of rare fish and other wildlife. The drought has brought all this to a head, touching off the sort of contentious water wars described by Mark Twain more than a century ago. In the West, the author reportedly remarked, "whiskey is for drinking; water is for fighting over."

Rising tensions. In places like Santa Fe, N.M., "water police" now patrol the streets handing out steep fines to scofflaws who violate watering restrictions. A recent 47 percent hike in water rates and the government-mandated retrofitting of 8,000 homes with low-flow toilets have helped reduce per capita water consumption to about 150 gallons a day. But with developers still building to accommodate a countywide population that has grown nearly 75 percent since 1980, tensions are rising. "People are getting sick and tired of bucketing water from their showers just so the developers can build the next big home or subdivision," says Patti Bushee, a Santa Fe city councilor.

In a recent showdown with developers, she and three other city councilors pushed for a new ordinance that would have put a temporary moratorium on construction. Her opponents, who ultimately defeated the measure, flooded the city with building permit applications in case it passed. "So now we have lots more new homes being built," complains Bushee, "but not enough water for the people who already live here."

Aurora resident Ed Wirth sees his lawn and backyard garden threatened this season, while his water bill surges as a result of summertime surcharges of up to 200 percent. "If things are really so bad, then shouldn't we just stop all the new construction, like right now?" Wirth asks.

With Aurora facing another parched summer, the answer might seem an emphatic "yes." Yet city water officials say the problem isn't new houses; it's the greenery surrounding them. According to Peter Binney, Aurora's utilities director, about half the city's water goes to landscape irrigation. "We don't have a water shortage," he says; "we have a water allocation crisis."

Increasingly, experts concur that new strategies for divvying up water are the key to resolving water problems. "The truth is, we've got oodles of water for urban growth," says Charles Howe, a water resources economist at the University of Colorado-Boulder. "Even if you buy just 10 percent of the agricultural water, you've got enough to double the supply for urban and industrial uses." Such transfers can require pipeline extensions and other tweaks to water delivery systems, as well as some swapping between the government agencies and utilities that manage much of the water's flow.

Cheaper, too. Yet they are far less expensive and controversial than the alternative: building big new dams and reservoirs. "The era of big new water projects is over," says Melinda Kassen, a water attorney with the river-protection group Trout Unlimited, which helped defeat Colorado's Two Forks Dam, one of the last big water projects proposed in the West. "It just so happens that it's far cheaper for cities to buy agricultural water."

Ron Aschermann and the other Rocky Ford Ditch shareholders are eager to sell. But some of their neighbors in the Arkansas Valley worry that transferring the water rights to Aurora would devastate the local economy. "Our lifestyle would literally dry up and blow away," says Bob Rawlings, publisher of the local newspaper, the Pueblo Chieftain, who has waged an angry campaign to stop the sale. "When you take water out of the valley, you rob us of our lifeblood. Without water, the farms dry up. Then all the businesses that rely on them go. Then the tax base and the economy go, too."

He points to nearby Crowley County, where farmers sold their water rights to cities 20 years ago. "They turned that beautiful farmland into a desert and the community into a bunch of derelict buildings," says Rawlings. He and other community activists have lobbied for state legislation to block water holders from transferring rights to buyers outside their areas. Others back stiffer laws requiring those transferring water to pay for economic losses to the community.

But such measures undermine farmers' incentive to use supplies more efficiently and hamper an open market for water, say some experts. If farmers can sell their water rights freely, "water will flow to its highest-valued use," says Bennett Raley, the Interior Department's assistant secretary for water and science. The agency's just announced Western Water Initiative promotes a market-based system where farmers can sell water rights (a step that now requires court approval) or temporarily lease them to "water banks," creating spot markets where water can be traded among farms, cities, and environmental interests. "In some years farmers will choose to grow crops," says Raley. "Other years they'll take a check."

That is what Raley envisions for southeastern California's arid Imperial Valley. Its farmers receive about a trillion gallons of water annually from the Colorado

River to water alfalfa and other crops. The irrigation project is among the nation's largest and least efficient. Things are about to change, however, because of new federally mandated reductions that require both the valley and neighboring San Diego (which also draws heavily from the river) to decrease their combined consumption by 15 percent.

Urban shift. Ed McGrew, an Imperial Valley farmer, is resigned to giving up some of his water. "Most of us realize it's inevitable that more water is going to be transferred from agriculture to cities," says McGrew, who runs a 1,400-acre farm near Holtville. To save water, he has already invested in a drip watering system for his asparagus field and pump-back systems to recirculate water used to irrigate his alfalfa crop. If San Diegans will pay Imperial Valley farmers to give up part of their allotment, "I'd have no problem taking my share of the money and investing in more conservation," he says.

But some of those who have spent a lifetime working the land are determined to hold on to every last drop. Along New Mexico's drought-plagued Rio Grande, for example, farmers threatened with federally enforced irrigation cuts to help save an endangered minnow have refused a government offer to pay them not to plant this season. "We don't want their money; we just want them to leave us alone and let us farm," says Corky Herkenhoff, who owns a 600-acre alfalfa farm near San Acacia.

The drought, however, may have hurt the farmers' case. With low river flows killing thousands of minnows, "the drought has dramatically raised public awareness about the plight of the river," says John Horning, executive director of the Forest Guardians, a Santa Fe-based nonprofit that has waged a legal campaign to help save the rare minnow. Horning points to a recent University of New Mexico study showing that 80 percent of state residents support measures to ensure the river's flow. "In the past, people didn't have to choose between an alfalfa field and a healthy river," says Horning, but now that they're forced to, "they're increasingly choosing the river."

With another meager mountain runoff this spring, Ken Maxey, a federal Bureau of Reclamation manager in Albuquerque, says he had little choice but to warn Rio Grande-area farmers that if they don't stop diverting river water he might have to force them to do so. "That's when the war is going to start around here," warns Herkenhoff. "We may not sit on the head gates with a shotgun, but we'll get out and raise some hell."

In fact, it may be all over but the shouting. Although the Old West holds prior claims to the region's water, the New West increasingly has the political and financial clout to determine how and where the water gets used. And as the continuing drought raises the stakes for everyone, more fields are likely to go fallow so that the Rio Grande's minnows can survive and people like Ed Wirth can keep their backyards green.

Crisis Conditions

Places where water wars may erupt or intensify in the next two decades as the demands of people, farms, and wildlife outstrip existing supplies.

	Unmet rural water needs	Moderate conflict potential	Substantial conflict potential	Highly likely conflict potential
Wash.		•	•	
Ore.		•	•	
Calif.	•	•	•	•
Idaho		•		
Nev.				•
Ariz.	•		•	•
Mont.		•		
Wyo.		•		
Utah	•			•
N.M.	•	•	•	•
Colo.	•	•		•
N.D.	•	•		
S.D.	•			
Neb.	•	•		
Kan.	•	•		
Okla.	•	•		
Texas	•	•	•	•

Source: U.S. Department of the Interior
Rob Cady—USN&WR

The Eternal Challenge; California's Water

A new nightmare for greens: conserving water may encourage sprawl

A CENTURY ago, William Mulholland scared up support in Los Angeles for an aqueduct to bring water from the Owens Valley. "If you don't get the water now, you'll never need it. The dead never get thirsty." Nowadays, the brutish water baron's bailiwick, the Los Angeles Department of Water and Power, merely "urges Los Angeles residents and businesses to take measures to conserve water during the hot weather."

That familiar advice, issued on August 1st after "brief water outages" in the West San Fernando Valley, will not be the last appeal to Angelenos' doubtful sense of civic responsibility. Back in Mulholland's day, Los Angeles had 200,000 residents; now it has 3.8m. The state's population is due to rise from 36m residents to 48m by 2030; and so will its thirst for water—to fill swimming pools, wash cars, water lawns, build golf courses and keep orchards from reverting to deserts.

Is this sustainable? A recent report from the Public Policy Institute of California reckons that if per capita urban use of water remains at its 2000 levels of 232 gallons per person per day, California will need another 3.6m acre feet of the stuff by 2030—a 40% increase on the current level. (An acre foot, almost 326,000 gallons, is the amount of water needed to cover one acre to a depth of one foot.)

Part of the challenge will be geography. Most Californians live in the arid southern bit of the state; the water they need comes from the Sierra Nevada mountains in the north and from California's share of the Colorado river to the east, which its fast-growing neighbours covet. It is not hard to see why greens bleat about California's growth being unsustainable.

However, California's real problem (as the PPIC report makes clear) remains not shortages but allocation and pricing. Farmers, who use up to 80% of California's water, deplore the demand that comes with urban sprawl; city-dwellers see no reason to be held hostage by the farmers, who employ no more than a million workers a year; and environmentalists accuse almost everyone in sight of both wasting water and polluting it.

Peace, of a sort, has broken out—the result of three changes in the aftermath of the 1987–92 drought. In 1994, state and federal agencies hashed out a deal to restore the Sacramento-San Joaquin Delta ecosystem while still ensuring a sufficient supply of water. In 2001, the state legislature passed two "show-me-the-water" bills that require developers first to prove they have access to water while still, as required by previous legislation, satisfying environmental worries. Finally, in 2003, another deal was brokered with six other states and the Department of the Interior, whereby California kept its access to the Colorado river but reduced its demand from more than 5m acre feet to the 4.4m acre-feet limit it had agreed to—and ignored—as long ago as 1929.

These deals might seem to put a limit on the state's sprawl. Perversely, however, the conservation measures that greens have long championed will now allow further expansion. Peter Gleick, of the Pacific Institute of Oakland, reckons that California could save 30% of its current urban water use simply by fully implementing existing conservation technologies.

Even small things can make a difference. The Metropolitan Water District, which distributes most of southern California's water, notes that people in Sacramento, which has no metering system, use 271 gallons a day; by contrast, per capita use in metered Los Angeles is just 155 gallons a day, not least because the water department has also installed 1.24m low-flush toilets since 1990. There is also water to be saved in delivery systems: according to the Department of the Interior, each dollar spent modernising a canal brings a return of up to $5 in conserved water.

Then there is the issue of pricing. Stephanie Pincetl, a visiting professor at the University of California, Los Angeles, argues that more places should adopt progressive pricing (the more you use, the higher the rate). Sprinkler-dotted Beverly Hills, which is notoriously profligate, has just added a fourth tier to its pricing structure.

The most obvious opportunity for better pricing and better conservation, however, is in farming, especially in the vast Central Valley. The federally financed Central Valley Project is the largest irrigation system in the country, supplying some 20,000 farms with enough water to serve ten cities the size of Los Angeles. But whereas the cities have to pay anything from $400 to $600 for each acre foot, a Central Valley farmer may pay only $80.

The farmers point out that they are closer to the source and do not have to pay the transport and purification costs that the cities have to bear. But they are also massively subsidised: they pay no interest on the capital cost of the irrigation project, now more than 50 years old. Indeed, given the small amount of principal so far repaid, Barry Nelson of the National Resources Defence Council reckons the valley's farmers are enjoying what amounts to a 500-year interest-free loan—quite apart from cheap energy and subsidies for pasture land and for growing low-price crops such as cotton, rice and alfalfa.

Hence a fundamental problem: as long as America wants California to be its breadbasket, providing produce that can be grown much more cheaply elsewhere in the world, California's farmers will need cheap water—and if their water is cheap, they have no incentive to conserve it. Why, for example, should they invest in expensive sub-surface drip-feed irrigation when they can simply let water flood across a field?

Conservation does not solve everything—and it can have unintended consequences. Ms Pincetl notes, for example, that re-lining the All-American Canal to stop seepage into the groundwater affected the wetlands south of the border with Mexico—and resulted in a lawsuit by a Mexican NGO against America's Department of the Interior. And, for the true gloomsters, there is always global warming: if the snows that fall on the Sierra Nevada are replaced by rain, too much of California's water supply will run off to the sea instead of sinking into the groundwater. Then the battle between the cities and the farmers would turn really nasty.

The Other Stem Cells

Bernadine P. Healy

Like children, human embryonic stem cells are filled with potential but difficult to control. Since they were first isolated in 1998 from human embryos only a few days old, these primordial cells have achieved both fame and notoriety. Removed from their tightly programmed life as an embryo, they can multiply indefinitely in the lab in primitive form or they can be coaxed to differentiate into virtually any cell in the body—a nest of beating heart cells, for example. But inject them into intact animals, and they are just as likely to be rejected by the immune system or turned into a deadly tumor filled with teeth, hair, and random cells.

These untamed primitive cells are important because they're a potential inroad to cures for devastating diseases like Parkinson's, diabetes, heart failure, and Alzheimer's. Their promise has stirred the imagination of the public, ignited the fervor of Nancy Reagan and others wounded by such illnesses, and attracted piles of money from government, commercial investors, and philanthropists. And the view that embryonic stem cells per se are forbidden fruit—as argued by abortion opponents—may be softening. Just last week, over 250 members of Congress, including avowed "pro-lifers," came out in support of using taxpayer money on the estimated 400,000 frozen spare embryos, stored in fertility clinics, that might otherwise be destroyed.

But all this hoopla fails to confront the real issue, which is not about using spare embryos. Rather it's about giving scientists license to make living human embryos from scratch—through IVF or human cloning—that is part and parcel of the long-term pursuit of therapeutically usable embryonic stem cells. This is the hidden but ever so hot issue on which there is no consensus, either in Congress or among the states. California has a voter referendum in November to issue a $3 billion bond to support stem-cell research, including therapeutic cloning. Other states have outlawed this approach entirely. Even the European Parliament and the United Nations have failed to agree whether therapeutic cloning is blessed or sinful.

What may be saving embryonic stem cells from the political quagmire are their increasingly compelling distant cousins, adult stem cells, which are quickly making regenerative medicine a dramatic reality. Until recently these cells have been largely ignored because they were thought to have limited regenerative value. But that has changed, in part because of the fuss and money surrounding embryo research. These less primitive but more stable cells exist in small quantities in all body organs. They won't be rejected and won't cause uncontrolled cell growth, and are therefore preferred for patient therapy. Of particular interest are the ones that

Bernadine P. Healy, "The Other Stem Cells" in *U.S. News & World Report*, vo. 136, no. 121, June 14, 2004, p. 77. Copyright © 2004 by U.S. News & World Report, L.P. Reprinted with permission.

nest in the bone marrow; they have the ability to transform into almost any tissue in the body.

Network. We are just learning that in the body, adult stem cells are players in a highly disciplined ballet. Indeed, they are key elements in a repair network in which wounded tissue sends out molecular SOS signals that mobilize stem cells in the affected organ and at the same time recruit bone marrow stem cells to home into the injury site. This may lead to a slow but natural replacement of tissues over time. Just last month a study in Lancet from the University of Florida reported that women who had had bone-marrow transplants from male donors were found—at autopsy months to years later—to have low levels of neurons of male origin, i.e., brain cells with Y chromosomes. Similar findings in both humans and animals suggest that stem cells may be replenishing other organs as well. A critical research question is whether or not these self-replenishing powers can be made to work faster and better, perhaps through drugs that stimulate stem-cell multiplication. Research already has some promising results.

Does this mean that embryonic stem cells should be abandoned? Absolutely not. They are powerful models for understanding how basic stem cells function. And it's entirely too early to give up on any form of stem cell that might have therapeutic value in the long run. But the meteoric ascent of adult cells as viable options for therapy, and the possibility of more spare embryos for research together provide breathing room for a much-needed public debate. There remain many unresolved social, ethical, and legal issues regarding the creation of embryos and clones for research. Not the least of these is the potential for exploitation of young women to get fresh eggs for this work and the lack of boundaries for research on embryos when it's conducted privately.

A stem-cell biologist recently quipped to me that our children may live forever because of stem-cell work, but we are certain to die. We don't have forever for this crucial debate.

Nancy's Next Campaign; The Former First Lady's Passion for Stem-Cell Research Has Fueled a Political Battle. Where Does the Science Stand?

Claudia Kalb; Debra Rosenberg

One spring afternoon in 2002, eight long years into her husband's descent into Alzheimer's, Nancy Reagan went to her friend Doug Wick's home in Los Angeles for a Hollywood-style tutorial on stem cells. Along with Wick and his wife, Lucy, both producers, the cast included moviemakers Jerry and Janet Zucker, actor Warren Beatty and Dr. Richard Klausner, now head of global health at the Bill & Melinda Gates Foundation. Nancy Reagan already knew a bit about stem cells—a year earlier, she'd written a letter to President Bush asking him to support embryonic research—but she was eager to delve deeper. Together the group discussed the ethics, the politics and the science. "She asked a lot of questions about what [stem cells] were, where they came from," says Klausner. Nancy knew it was too late to rescue her husband, but she "had a higher purpose," says Wick. "She feels the greatest legacy her family could ever have is to spare other families from going through what they have."

After the meeting, Nancy began making her views known behind the scenes, respectfully but forcefully—calling politicians, conversing with scientists, button-holing lawmakers at the rare Washington dinner she allowed herself. Then last month Reagan decided to go public at a Juvenile Diabetes Research Foundation gala, and she asked others to join in her quest. "Science has presented us with a hope called stem-cell research, which may provide our scientists with answers that have so long been beyond our grasp," she said. "I just don't see how we can turn our backs on this—there are just so many diseases that can be cured, or at least helped. We have lost so much time already, and I just really can't bear to lose any more."

Nancy Reagan's bold challenge to her own Republican Party and to Bush's 2001 policy on embryonic research was a pivotal moment for stem-cell advocates. For months they had been rallying across the country; with Nancy's support, and now with her husband's death and heroic farewell, they have found fresh momentum. Last week in Washington, 58 senators, including John Kerry, sent a letter to the White House, urging Bush to relax his restrictions on embryonic-stem-cell research. In a radio address to the nation over the weekend, Kerry reaffirmed his commitment to overturning Bush's policy if elected. On the West Coast, meanwhile, Californians for Stem Cell Research and Cures celebrated the collection of 1 million signatures authorizing a $3 billion stem-cell-research initiative to be put to the vote in November. In Boston 1,400 scientists gathered to discuss both embryonic and adult stem cells at a meeting of the International Society for Stem Cell Research (ISSCR), where the embryonic-stem-cell advocate and Republican senator Arlen Specter encouraged them to stand up for science. "We need more political activism," he told the group. "The marvels of modern science should obviously not be shackled." Newspapers ran editorials calling on Bush to honor Ronald Reagan's legacy by revising his stem-cell policy—"George should do it for the Gipper," said one—and a New York congressman introduced the Ronald Reagan Memorial Stem Cell Research Act of 2004.

All of this infuriated embryonic opponents: one senior Republican aide said naming stem-cell legislation after the president, who was ardently opposed to abortion, was "unbelievably shameless." But out of respect for Reagan, the adversaries mostly held their fire. Bush stayed mum, but privately officials said he would not budge on his opposition to destroying human embryos for the sake of science. "No dramatic advance, no scientific development will change the ethical principle" underlying Bush's position, a senior administration official told NEWSWEEK last week. Laura Bush, whose father died of Alzheimer's, made the media rounds instead, gently reiterating the administration's position on stem-cell research without attacking Nancy head-on. "We have to be really careful between what we want to do for science and what we should do ethically," she told CBS. When she was asked if she would endorse additional stem-cell research, the answer was clear: "No."

What is it about embryonic stem cells? How can these microscopic flecks galvanize scientists and celebrities and, at the same time, pit First Ladies against each other and turn political allies into formidable foes? Under the microscope, embryonic stem cells look like luminous stars in a black-and-white galaxy. Just days old, they have the extraordinary capacity to become any one of the more than 200 cell types that make up the human body—from heart to brain to muscle. Researchers believe they may hold the key to curing or at least revolutionizing our understanding of deadly diseases like Parkinson's, diabetes and Alzheimer's. But no matter how mysterious or magical their powers, the cells are culled from human embryos, and to those who consider the fusion of sperm and egg sacred life—whether it takes place in a womb or a lab dish—they are morally off-limits for research.

In an effort to placate both scientists and pro-life constituents, Bush announced a compromise policy on Aug. 9, 2001: federal funds, which underwrite the vast majority of scientific research in this country, could be used to study embryonic stem cells, but only those that had already been isolated in the lab and grown into stem-cell "lines." Almost immediately scientists began complaining that the restrictions would inhibit their work. The administration said as many as 78 lines existed, but that number turned out to be inflated; as of last week only 19 were available. (Other lines exist but can be worked on only with private money.) Scientists say the lines are often difficult to obtain and of questionable quality. "It's like forcing us to work with Microsoft version 1.0 when the rest of the world is already working with 6.2," says biologist David Anderson of Caltech. Without better access to embryonic stem cells, U.S. scientists worry that they're in danger of becoming bystanders to medical innovation.

Political support for embryonic-stem-cell research—galvanized by testimony from scientists and the heart-wrenching stories of sick Americans pleading for cures—has come from surprising quarters. Rep. Duke Cunningham, a pro-life Republican from California, says he is haunted by a child who told him, "Congressman, you're the only person who can save my life." He signed on after a scientist explained that IVF clinics house thousands of frozen embryos, from which stem cells are derived, and that many are destined to be discarded. "My own personal belief is that I'm actually saving life from something that is not going to be life," he says. Sen. Orrin Hatch, a Mormon from Utah who is staunchly pro-life, is an ardent supporter, too. In early 2003 he, Specter and Democratic senators Ted Kennedy, Dianne Feinstein and Tom Harkin introduced a bill that, with strict regulations, would allow so-called therapeutic cloning to create new embryos from which more stem cells could be harvested. Along the way, Nancy Reagan spoke with both Republican senators and sent Hatch a note backing the legislation. "She's a conservative woman, very much like her husband," says Hatch. "The fact that she's been willing to speak out on this has been very helpful."

Today 4.5 million Americans suffer from Alzheimer's, a number that is expected to spike to 16 million by 2050. Scientists and drug companies are rushing to improve diagnosis and treatment with brain imaging, medications and even an experimental vaccine. But as Nancy Reagan knows better than anyone, available therapies address symptoms only and are unable to halt the ravaging disease, let alone cure it altogether. That's where her passion for stem cells comes in. Already researchers have been able to coax embryonic stem cells into neurons that produce dopamine, the culprits in Parkinson's. Might scientists also find a way to transform them into the neurons damaged by Alzheimer's, then transplant the healthy new cells into a patient's brain? Nobody knows. The reality is that Alzheimer's is so complicated that even miraculous stem cells might not cure it. Harvard neurologist Rudy Tanzi likens the Alzheimer's brain to a defunct stereo. You can't "throw in a bunch of capacitors and transistors and expect to hear music," he says. "You have to rewire the system."

Maria Shriver, whose father has Alzheimer's and who has forged an alliance with Nancy Reagan on stem cells, believes the research could help uncover the illness's genetic link: "It will help millions of children of people with this disease." At the University of California, San Diego, Dr. Larry Goldstein is using embryonic stem cells to develop human brain cells that carry Alzheimer's mutations. Rather than analyze the disease in its later stages, he wants to watch it develop from the beginning, with the hope of creating drugs to stop its progress early on. Ultimately, scientists believe embryonic stem cells will be able to shine a light on the fundamentals of human biology. "It's not just that stem cells will magically cure disease, they can help us understand how life emerges," says stem-cell researcher Ron McKay of the National Institutes of Health. "This is the future of medicine."

When stem cells are involved, however, the future of medicine is never just about medicine—it's about politics, too. Scientific studies become ammunition to support a particular viewpoint; medical data, no matter how nuanced, get spun with political finesse. Now adult stem cells, derived from mature human beings rather than days-old embryos, have become pawns in the debate. The administration and right-to-life groups praise their potential, offering them up as equally powerful as embryonic stem cells, if not more so. Several years ago, research backed those claims, suggesting that adult stem cells were indeed far more "plastic" than anyone had dreamed. But now some scientists are challenging those findings. "People are starting to realize that the science of plasticity is not all there," says Dr. Leonard Zon, ISSCR president.

Unlike embryonic stem cells, adult stem cells are prewired to become a particular kind of tissue—skin, intestine or blood, for example. Like theatrical understudies, they stand in the wings, rushing in only when cells need replenishment after injury or disease. Scientists know the most about the adult stem cells of the blood, which are given in bone-marrow transplants to patients with cancer or blood diseases. That success prompted researchers to wonder: could adult blood stem cells have the same acrobatic ability as embryonic stem cells? Dr. Markus Grompe, of Oregon Health & Science University, initially thought yes. In 2000 he reported that adult blood stem cells were able to turn into liver cells in mice. But two years later Grompe reassessed his data and came to a different conclusion: the blood cells had fused with existing liver cells—more a case of biological identity theft than transformation.

New studies are now questioning earlier work on heart disease, too. In 2001, news that adult bone-marrow stem cells had become cardiac muscle in mice spurred great hope, even leading to clinical trials in humans. Dr. Piero Anversa, of New York Medical College, worked on the original research and stands by it "1,000 percent." But in April two groups reported that they could not reproduce the finding, a critical step in the validation of science. "Our paper says it doesn't work," says Stanford University's Dr. Irv Weissman.

The holy grail for many scientists is a cure for type 1 diabetes, the disease that plagues Doug Wick's daughter and helped spark Nancy Reagan's interest in stem cells. For years researchers have searched for adult stem cells in the pancreas, hoping such cells could make themselves into insulin-producing beta cells, which diabetics lack. But last month Harvard biologist Doug Melton dashed the hopes of many when he reported that he could find no adult stem cells in the pancreas at all. His conclusion: "If you want to make more beta cells, the place to look is embryonic stem cells."

Stem-cell science is still early in development—too early to make absolute statements about what works and what doesn't. Even the most passionate supporters of embryonic research believe the study of adult stem cells should proceed with equal vigor. Embryonic stem cells are the gold standard in versatility, but adult stem cells still hold promise, especially for repair within their own tissue family. A patient with Alzheimer's might benefit from a transplant of adult brain cells from a healthy donor. Or perhaps one day in the future, a drug might be able to jump-start sleeping adult stem cells in a patient's own brain, spurring them to fix the damage. What the scientists want is for the politicians to stay out of their petri dishes.

Back in Washington, the political future of stem-cell medicine remains unclear. Last month Bush's domestic-policy adviser reiterated the president's stance in a meeting with Reps. Diana DeGette and Michael Castle, bipartisan architects of a House letter signed by more than 200 members urging Bush to relax his restrictions. This week, NEWSWEEK has learned, NIH Director Elias Zerhouni will sit down with them as well. "It's my hope that the president will revisit the issue," says Specter. Now that the week of Reagan mourning is over, the opposition is likely to take its gloves off. Republican Sen. Sam Brownback of Kansas, who authored a bill banning all forms of cloning—including for stem-cell research—will hold hearings next week on adult stem-cell research, a meeting postponed in honor of Reagan's memorial. "There will be plenty of support for President Bush to continue the policy he has," says American Values president Gary Bauer. The White House, meanwhile, was working hard to downplay the differences between Nancy Reagan and the president. "Reasonable people can disagree," said one senior official.

Nancy Reagan knows she may not get what she wants on the first try, but Ken Duberstein, her husband's former chief of staff, says she won't give up. "She's not backing off," says Duberstein, "because this can be a living legacy of Ronald Reagan." And as Nancy herself has said, she doesn't have time to lose.

Kleber Offers Expert and Blunt Opinions on Addiction

Herbert Kleber, psychiatrist; Constance Holden

Kleber Offers Expert and Blunt Opinions on Addiction Yale University psychiatrist Herbert Kleber seems to be made to order for the job of deputy to drug chief William Bennett. Widely respected in his field, he has 25 years of experience in research and the administration of treatment programs. His own pioneering research focused on drugs to block addictive craving. He is also a registered Republican—a rarity for a Yale professor, much less a psychiatrist.

Kleber took an indefinite leave from Yale to be Bennett's "deputy for demand reduction" in the President's drug war, which is much sniped at by other academics for being wrong-headed and underfunded. However, a Yale colleague, psychiatrist David Musto, says Kleber knows "what it takes to make things work."

Kleber is not shy about his accomplishments. "I am considered one of the leading experts on treatment and policy aspects of substance abuse." Like his boss, Kleber has a sizable portfolio of blunt opinions. Of needle exchange programs, he says, "Morality aside, it won't work." He cites data from England showing that only 60% of clients came back after the first visit and 20% after the tenth, indicating "impulsive" addicts are unlikely to comply. As for the supposed futility of criminal punishment, he responds, "Criminologists say deterrence does work if applied swiftly and surely," but the present system offers little deterrence because so few suspects end up in jail. On pregnant women addicts, Kleber says those already in trouble with the law could be compelled to stay in a treatment facility for the duration of the pregnancy. The others pose a "much harder" question.

Kleber is unequivocal on the subject of drug legalization. Most advocates of the policy, he says, waffle when asked whether they would permit cocaine sales, which Kleber says would be an unqualified disaster. Government-regulated prices would not drive out drug crime, he argues, because if prices were kept up, illegal trade would continue to flourish, and if they were kept down, cocaine would be put "in the reach of every third grader." He believes crime would become more widespread and there would be more drug-associated violence because crack, in particular, causes "paranoia, irritability, and the need for action." Furthermore, he thinks legalization would result in rampant cocaine addiction, maybe even approaching alcoholism in scope.

Kleber's job centers on drug abuse treatment, prevention, and research. One of his major tasks will be prodding states to formulate systematic plans. Although many people have called for radical increases in funding for treatment, Kleber says the system is going to have to be improved first. One immediate need, he says, is for more "accountability." Quality reviews may be handled by a new branch of the Alcohol, Drug Abuse and Mental Health Administration, the Office of Treatment Improvement, which will administer demonstration programs and grants to states.

Many think that treatment should be provided for all addicts. But Kleber points out that there are many who don't want help and many others who will fail to benefit even if offered it. Of the 4 million estimated heavy drug users, Kleber thinks about 1 million fall in this category. Another 1 million are sufficiently motivated to stop on their own. The drug strategy is aimed at the remaining 2 million who might benefit from treatment.

Another big issue in treatment is "co-morbidity," the fact that recent studies show a high proportion of drug abusers also suffer from some psychopathology such as depression or schizophrenia. "Most programs don't have the capacity or sophistication" to treat such problems, says Kleber, who thinks treatment centers should be better coordinated with mental health providers.

Furthermore, "most of the treatment money out there now is for heroin," but the big problem now is cocaine, which is being regularly used by close to 3 million people. Despite the special challenges posed by crack addition, Kleber says the main reason it is so difficult to treat is "because of who's using it." There is not much leverage available from "competing reinforcers"—that is, inner city crack addicts are less likely to have jobs, families, and reputations at stake.

A Familiar Debate: Jail or Treatment?

Mark Steil

The effects of methamphetamine use are working their way through our criminal justice system. The rapid rise in meth arrests is one of the main factors in sharply higher prison populations. The cost of housing drug offenders has renewed an old debate—what works best, prison or treatment? The debate over state drug policies came into sharp focus this year in a case involving methamphetamine, jail time and a young Minnesota mother.

St. Paul, Minn.—The numbers tell a troublesome story. About 40 percent of the state's felony drug convictions involve methamphetamine. That's more than 1,300 cases. About 90 percent of those offenders spend time behind bars in local jails or state prisons.

Minnesota corrections officials can feel the explosion. Inmates convicted of a drug charge, including meth, make up about one-fourth of the 7,600 adults in prison. That number has doubled in just six years.

Amber Bluhm is one of those heading to jail. Bluhm, 22, faces a six-month sentence after pleading guilty to methamphetamine possession. It's her second meth conviction. She also pleaded guilty to possession in 1999. In the days before she's sent away, she regrets her drug use.

"I'd love to go back to high school. I'd do it all over, I'd go to prom, I'd be in more sports," says Bluhm. "I missed everything. I missed my graduation ceremony. I missed living."

A church-going, small-town girl, Bluhm once considered herself "goody-goody." She says her path to jail began with cigarettes. Marijuana followed, then methamphetamine. Her life was filled with tragedy. She says two of her friends killed themselves because of meth.

Bluhm says she hasn't used meth for two years, but still feels the effects. She hears and sees things that aren't there. She warns teenagers to stay away from meth.

"If they don't want to hear voices and stuff, then they shouldn't use," says Bluhm. "If they don't want to hear the insanity and the craziness. It's evil. I pray every day that it will go away."

That's not all she's dealing with. The mother of a 2-year-old son, Bluhm is scared to go to jail. She pleaded guilty two years ago to her second meth charge, but is free while she appeals. She argues jail is too harsh a punishment—that it will do more harm than good, and punish her son as well. Bluhm says she's beat her addiction. She went through drug treatment, finished high school and held a job.

"I'm sober now, and I don't see why I need to get punished for being an addict—when I got help. Now it's just going to make things worse for me," Bluhm says. "I've straightened my life up and my life's going great. Now I'm just going to go to jail, everything's just going to fall apart on me again, and I've got to pick it up again when I get out of jail."

That's a real life summary of the anti-prison, pro-treatment argument. It's gaining support from some influential members of Minnesota government.

Amber Bluhm's appeal went to the Minnesota Supreme Court. The court upheld Bluhm's six-month jail sentence, but not without reservation. The court said Minnesota law requires jail time for a second drug conviction. But the justices also noted their "disfavor" with mandatory sentences. Many feel it takes away their discretion.

In a separate opinion, Associate Justice James Gilbert said Bluhm "has turned her life around." Noting her sobriety, Gilbert wrote, "Bluhm has done everything the criminal justice system could hope for." Gilbert said given that progress, jail time for Bluhm was "unnecessary" and "harsh." He agreed, however, that because of the way state drug laws are written, Amber Bluhm must go to jail.

Justice Gilbert would not comment directly on the Bluhm case. But he did talk about how Minnesota's criminal justice system is being tested by the increase in drug arrests.

"There's no question that the problem is there. And it's not going to go away if we just pretend it's not there. It's been there for a long time, in some counties it's getting worse," says Gilbert. "Now methamphetamine in greater Minnesota is the drug of choice, and in my opinion that's almost like an epidemic."

Justice Gilbert says the state should look for alternatives to imprisonment. He promotes the use of drug courts. Currently there are seven drug courts operating in Minnesota. In a drug court, offenders are sent to treatment. Gilbert says there is a powerful incentive for offenders to complete the program.

"They realize if they step out of bounds and don't follow the mercy—if you will—that has been granted them by the court, they're going to be going into jail real quick," says Gilbert.

The sheer cost of imprisonment is incentive for some to rethink state drug laws. Rep. Eric Lipman, R-Lake Elmo, says too many people are being imprisoned. He says Minnesota taxpayers will pay another $300 million in prison costs over the next 10 years, unless it changes drug sentencing.

Lipman says Minnesota drug laws are among the harshest in the nation. A person can spend more than seven years in jail for possessing 25 grams of meth. That's the weight of 25 paper clips. In most other states, the sentence would be one year behind bars.

"So we are many, many times higher then most every place else in the U.S.," says Lipman, "in ways that I think are very expensive to the taxpayer and corrosive to the community, in comparison with what deterrent effect we're getting and what rehabilitative effect we're getting."

Lipman says without adequate treatment, many offenders start using drugs as soon as they're released. Lipman has tried, without luck, to get the Legislature to send more people to treatment instead of jail.

A report by the Minnesota Sentencing Guidelines Commission says treatment would save money. The study says prison costs the state nearly $30,000 a year per inmate, while the cost of treatment is just over $4,000.

But those against relaxing drug laws say something more important than money is at risk. Rep. John Lesch, DFL-St. Paul, says easing penalties will lead to more drug use. Lesch says any relaxation of state law is basically a free sales pitch for the drug industry.

"It strikes me as the Wal-Mart bill for drug dealers," says Lesch. "You know—low, low prices for buying in bulk."

Lesch works as a prosecutor for the city of St. Paul. He says judges have enough leeway now to deal with drug offenders. He says judges often give lighter sentences for drug crimes then state law recommends.

The Sentencing Guidelines Commission report offers support for that claim. About half the people convicted of manufacturing meth receive a lighter sentence then called for in state guidelines. In fact, the report says, judicial departure from state recommended sentences has been "consistently high" for drug offenses. But not in all cases.

Amber Bluhm awaits jail time, even though one state Supreme Court justice said that sentence amounts to "unmitigated harshness." Bluhm says it sends a signal.

"I'm one of the few that did straighten up and I did get my life together. Went to treatment. I've been trying to go to school and everything else. And I feel like they're just telling me that's not good enough. Like who cares if you get sober, you're still a piece of crap," says Bluhm.

That sense of worthlessness is the kind of attitude that can contribute to more drug use. Bluhm says that won't happen to her, she says her son is all the incentive she needs to stay away from methamphetamine.

But many others fall victim to the drug time after time. That means more crime, and offers state lawmakers a challenge—spend money for more prisons, or take the politically risky step of sending more offenders to treatment instead.

How Noise Pollution Affects Whales;
Sonar Study Tunes in to Underwater Racket

Eric Alan Barton

The sperm whale made famous in stories like "Moby Dick" is one of the most talkative mammals in the sea.

It sends out clicks strung together similar to Morse code, repeated among chatty packs of whales around the globe.

But sperm whales exposed to booming man-made noises stay mysteriously quiet for as long as two days. Without the clicking—batlike sonar the whales also use to hunt and navigate—they might not be able to eat or find their way.

Researchers fear underwater noise pollution could be hurting the whales and possibly other underwater mammals. Scientists will launch a first-of-its-kind study next month in waters off Southwest Florida to gauge the damage of booming noises on underwater mammals.

If the study shows noise pollution injures whales, it could spark new rules to reduce man-made sounds produced by seaward shipping, the oil industry and even the Navy.

The Navy is trying to defend its proposed low-frequency sonar, which blasts intense noises to find enemy submarines. Tests of the equipment in the Bahamas last year have been blamed for the rare beaching of two dozen beaked whales. Bleeding from the ears, about five of the whales died.

Likewise, the engines of supertankers and massive cargo ships that travel the world produce droning noises that are deafening at close range.

But the oil industry is blamed for the noisiest business in the Gulf of Mexico. The industry uses sonar equipment that emits booming noises to find buried oil. The sonar emits a blast loud enough to give whales concussions from deafening shock waves.

Researchers will test the damage caused by those shock waves during several expeditions this year, including a month-long trip starting March 15. Scientists from several universities and research facilities will attach suction cup noise sensors to dozens of sperm whales between Key West and Southwest Florida. The suction cups will allow them to listen to the noises whales hear underwater and to monitor the clicking speech of the whales.

During another expedition this summer, scientists will set off the same booming sonar equipment the oil industry uses, near the whales. The tests could determine whether the sound causes whales to stop clicking, and if so, whether it keeps them from hunting and communicating.

"Any animal that relies on communication to find prey and to communicate with each other could be lost without it," said Doug Nowacek, a Mote Marine Laboratory oceanographer who helped develop the suction-cup sensor.

Scientists tested the noise sensors last year on whales near the mouth of the Mississippi River. Next month's expedition will be the first time they will collect data. It is one of several expeditions planned in the next two years to study the 600 sperm whales believed to live in the Gulf.

The four-year, $4 million research is being paid for in part by the Navy, the Mineral Management Service, which oversees the lease of oil deposits in U.S. waters, and the National Marine Fisheries Service, which makes regulations to protect endangered animals.

The agencies could enact rules restricting most types of noise pollution in the Gulf and all U.S. waters, but just how restrictive those rules could be isn't clear. Federal law protects endangered animals, but enacting restrictions to quiet cargo ships, for instance, would be difficult to enforce.

Instead, researchers are concentrating on the oil industry's sonar equipment, which is used by as many as a dozen boats mapping the Gulf floor at any given time. The sonar uses air guns that create an air bubble in the water, causing a 250-decibel explosion when it pops. The sound waves reach 30,000 feet to the Gulf floor and are reflected back to the oil-seeking ships above. The sound waves bounce off layers of rock and gravel, allowing them to see a cross section of sediment where oil could be located.

The air guns produce noises several hundred times louder than the minimum noise that causes permanent ear damage to marine mammals, said Marsha Green, president of the Ocean Mammal Institute.

"A deaf whale is a dead whale," said Green, a professor at Albright College in Pennsylvania. "They use hearing to navigate and communicate, so if they're deaf, they're going to die."

The oil industry could switch to a sonar system that uses less-harmful vibrations instead of bursts of sound, but switching to the new equipment would cost millions, said Bill Dragoset, with London-based WesternGeco, one of the largest users of the air guns.

Like WesternGeco, companies using sonar air guns would pass on those costs to the oil companies that pay for the tests. But oil companies are large enough, with profits in the billions of dollars, that the costs would not affect the price consumers pay at the pump for gas, Dragoset said.

"The oil and gas industry usually goes by what's cheapest," said Terry Henwood, with the National Marine Fisheries Service. "If we find that they're causing damage to the whales, we will move to protect them."

The damage caused to sperm whales could be as simple as pushing them out of their typical habitat after they are spooked by loud noises, said Peter Tyack, a senior scientist at Woods Hole Oceanographic Institution in Massachusetts.

But proving that could be tough because the 60-foot whales, which may migrate thousands of miles, are so difficult to study, Tyack said. Female whales are believed to live in the Gulf in packs, while males may migrate to mate.

The 50-ton sperm whales are being used instead of other underwater mammals because the research will help scientists better understand the elusive mammals. Sperm whales dive thousands of feet deep to feed, presumably on giant squid, and there's little research on how their clicking is used to find prey.

In response, researchers next month also will attach tags to track the whales over six months to see if they flee after being scared by loud noises.

A sperm whale pushed from an area in fear of human noises could lose the groups or family in which it usually travels.

"Sperm whales are very social," Nowachek said, "and contact is one of those things that is very important to their survival."

Staff writer Eric Alan Barton can be reached at 742-6167 or eric.barton@herald-trib.com.

Sonar Ban Sounded Good: A Skeptical Analysis

Jennifer Linn Jacquet

In what appeared to be a triumph for environmentalists, in 2003 a U.S. court limited the Navy's use of low-frequency activated sonar (LFA) to safeguard endangered marine species from its blare. After millions of dollars, years of research, and a lengthy trial with questionable use of science, the ruling appeared to be a whale of a victory. Now the courtrooms are quiet, one boat's sonar has been silenced, and only a human-made aquatic cacophony remains.

The U.S. Navy uses LFA technology to detect enemy submarines. "Submarines have gotten really quiet. You can't listen for them anymore. You have to actually put energy into the ocean to get a reflection back and determine where they are," explained scientist Chris Clark, director of the Bioacoustics Research Program at Cornell University. "You have to build an acoustic lighthouse. The only way to get the energy far enough in the water is to go lower in frequency. It's all driven by physics."

The Navy has only one boat with active LFA technology, which consists of 18 loudspeakers, each the size of a small bathtub. The speakers are lowered 300-500 feet in the water and broadcast tones at about 230 decibels.

LFA travels hundreds to thousands of miles. Some scientists and environmentalists believe that LFA adversely affects the behavior of fish and marine mammals. Conservationists are particularly concerned that LFA jeopardizes whales, since they use acoustics to feed, travel, mate, and detect predators.

For this reason, the Natural Resources Defense Council (NRDC), famous for endangered species litigation, took the U.S. Navy to court. Using compelling laws such as the Marine Mammal Protection Act and the Endangered Species Act, NRDC and other environmental groups sought a permanent injunction that would prevent the Navy's peacetime use of the LFA sonar.

"In this particular case, we became aware that the U.S. Navy was on the verge of deploying a very, very powerful new low frequency sonar (LFA) without having done any environmental review and certainly without having obeyed any laws to which they're subject," said Andrew Wetzler, an NRDC lead attorney on the case.

Despite objections from the Navy, who argued that prohibiting peacetime use of LFA sonar would threaten national security, a California judge ruled in NRDC's favor. (Though in times of war or heightened threat, the Navy is free to use LFA sonar without restriction.)

"Certainly this is one of the most important cases that we've been involved in because it involves such a cutting edge and poorly understood problems—that is the effect that undersea noise can have on marine life," commented Wetzler.

LFA does seem to be poorly understood.

Chris Clark was one of the principal scientists involved with the LFA studies funded by the Navy. (Croll, Donald, Christopher Clark, John Calambokidis, William Edison, and Bernie R. Tershy. 2001. "Effect of anthropogenic low-frequency noise on the foraging ecology of Balaenoptera whales." Animal Conservation 4, 13-27.) Clark began his work in acoustics over thirty years ago with Roger Payne—who is to whales what Louis Leakey was to primates. Clark is now one of the leading marine mammal acoustics scientists. His office is crammed with books on marine mammal sounds while photographs of whales and back issues of Animal Conservation line the hallway of his lab.

"There is one thing that I feel pretty confident about," said Clark. "We saw no immediately obvious negative reaction of animals to LFA. We weren't getting any strong results indicating that there was some massive response. This was contradictory to what we expected."

Clark told a story about a study of LFA done off of Hawaii. A top scientist who specializes in whale song listened with a hydrophone, an underwater microphone, to humpback song as the ship emitted LFA. Clark waited to see the scientist's response and, after fifteen seconds of LFA transmission, Clark finally brought the noise to the scientist's attention. The scientist had mistaken LFA for just another singing humpback.

Clark explained that it is not entirely surprising that whales do not exhibit an immediate response to LFA. After all, LFA emits at around 230 decibels, but lightning strikes and volcanic eruptions—sounds whales have heard since time immemorial—are even louder. And while LFA travels hundreds of miles, so too do the sounds from storms and shipping. Ocean shipping in Asia, for instance, can be heard off" the coast of California.

"[LFA] is not a sound that would typically trigger a response of: 'Oh my god, here comes a predator,'" said Clark. "When you listen to it, it's not like a killer whale. Harm, physical harm, would only occur if you were really, really close to the flat. The perception of [LFA] being this enormous, nasty, ear-splitting thing is a bit exaggerated."

But NRDC disagreed that LFA is innocuous and recruited many scientists to voice their opposition during the trial. The mass media, too, portrayed LFA as extremely hazardous. In a 1999 article in *USA Today*, a reporter wrote, "After noise pollution from shipping, LFA is of greatest concern among marine scientists." ("Navy sonar sends waves of concern worldwide", *USA Today*, Arlington: July 6, 1999, 8.)

"Many of my good friends raised [LFA] as a concern but they are poorly informed about acoustics in the ocean," explained Clark. "They've come at it from a purely biological point of view. They don't understand the physics of sound in the ocean. And we, as a community of biologists, have never addressed noise in the ocean."

LFA was confused during the trial with mid-frequency sonar—a decades old, louder technology used around the world. Wetzler and other NRDC lawyers submitted provocative evidence of beaked whale beachings and deaths in the Bahamas. The Navy's LFA ship, however, is off the coast of California.

Though mid-frequency sonar was implicated in the deaths of these whales, the beaked whale stranding was influential in the LFA case. In the final opinion, the judge wrote that, "The possibility that the stranding in the Bahamas, and other standings associated with military sonar, could foretell similar injuries from LFA is troubling. It would be more protective of marine mammals to adopt the plaintiffs (NRDC's) conservative approach to uncertainty and not deploy LFA sonar unless and until further scientific research rules out a similar impact from LFA sonar." (see the 73-page opinion of U.S. magistrate Elizabeth Laport, released August 26, 2003.)

After years of litigation, the Navy and NRDC ultimately negotiated a region of the ocean where LFA can be deployed and regions where it cannot. Despite studies that demonstrated that LFA is not disruptive to whales, lawyers, the media, and the public voiced opposition to LFA deployment on the whales' behalf.

Yet LFA is much more likely to damage the ears of fish, rather than whales. LFA may also harm fish swim bladders that regulate buoyancy. Furthermore, there are over 15,000 known species of fish in the world's oceans but only around 80 species of whales. Still, NRDC, other environmental groups, and the media linked the LFA hazard to the leviathans rather than fish.

"Whales are religious icons," explained Clark. Marine mammals often act as mascots for environmental campaigns because of their capacity to incite compassion.

Clark said he saw the LFA court case as a red herring for noise pollution in the ocean. He said he resented the face-off with conservationists, being badgered on the witness stand, and the accusation of biased results because his funding came from the Navy.

"I wanted to say, 'Wait a minute, I'm doing this because I am concerned there is a problem,'" said Clark. "But to me the science says it isn't as much of a concern as I originally thought."

After his scientific findings, Clark said he believes that conservationists should focus on other sources of noise pollution in the ocean rather than LFA.

"There are many other things in the ocean that are far more egregious than LFA," said Clark. "There are things that are going on day after day that are just insidious. Seismic exploration, ocean shipping—all these things are just out there all the time."

Mid-frequency sonar is one such thing. Mid-frequency sonar is more powerful than LFA and has been used for decades. Unlike LFA, a loud low-frequency sound that whales have been exposed to through earthquakes and storms, whales are unaccustomed to hearing mid-frequency sonar. And unlike LFA, active on only one boat, almost every navy around the globe uses mid-frequency sonar and uses it regularly. NRDC recognizes that sonar is a problem that transcends political boundaries.

"The solution to the proliferation of active sonar can't come from the United States alone," said Wetzler. "There's a real need for an international regime to regulate the use of peacetime sonar."

But it's not just sonar that needs regulating. Other sources of noise pollution in the ocean are largely ignored. Furthermore, all attempts at global management of the world's oceans have been more idyllic than practical. Without strict enforcement, it's likely that noise in the ocean will persist. In the meantime, LFA, harmful or not, alerted the public to the issue of sound in the marine environment.

"LFA has become a lightning rod for the conscientious objection to man putting intentionally loud sound into the ocean," said Clark. "If [the LFA case] raises consciousness about noise in the ocean or the ocean situation in general then that's good. It's good that the public has been made aware that human noise in the oceans is a potentially serious problem. And all the bickering in the courtroom just washes away."

Supplements Under Siege: Legislation Is Working Its Way Through Congress That Could Shelve Nutritional Supplements for Good

Jeff O'Connell

It won't make newspaper headlines until the battle is already lost, but the supplement industry is being attacked. And if you use supplements, so are you. The DHEA pill you just swallowed? Use it and soon you may see that acronym, minus the H, on the jacket of the federal agent cuffing you for using a controlled substance. The ephedra-free fat burner you're using to help shed a few pounds for a wedding or reunion? Find a good tailor instead. As for purchasing the hottest new supplement, you might as well hit car showrooms looking for an Edsel.

The threat to the supplement industry has arrived in the form of S. 722, a bill introduced to the Senate of the United States at the end of March by Illinois Sen. Richard Durbin. (Should it be passed into law, the bill would become the Dietary Supplement Safety Act of 2003.) The scenarios above are alarming but not alarmist. And while they may not be the intent of the senator, they are likely to be unintended consequences of legislation that uses the stimulant ephedra and hormone precursors as a Trojan horse for changing the way all supplements are regulated, principally by treating them as drugs rather than foods.

The Passage of Dshea

That seemingly innocuous distinction could be nothing less than the difference between the supplement industry surviving and withering away. That supplements are foods, not drugs, seems self-evident, but from a regulatory standpoint it wasn't codified until 1994, when Congress modified the Federal Food, Drug, and Cosmetic Act of 1938 by passing the Dietary Supplement Health and Education Act. It did so in response to a series of proposals made by the Food and Drug Administration that supplement companies felt would have limited the availability of their products to consumers.

"DSHEA has been very successful because it allowed consumers to have more access to products," says David Seckman, executive director and chief executive officer of the National Nutritional Foods Association, based in Newport Beach, Calif., the largest natural-products trade association. (For the record, NNFA opposes S. 722.) "Second, it provided the framework and statutory authority for the FDA to go ahead and protect consumers from products determined to be unsafe."

What DSHEA did not do is remove the FDA from supplement regulation, although you might think it did listening to the anti-supplement mantra of selected politicians, regulators and commentators, who conjure images of the industry as some sheriffless Wild West town filled with rogue chemists gunslinging whatever they want into bottles and pills.

"It is widely and erroneously believed that DSHEA eviscerated the FD&C Act safety requirements for dietary supplements," according to Peter Barton Hutt, partner in the Washington, D.C., law firm Covington & Burling and former chief counsel for the FDA. "DSHEA actually provides greater FDA scrutiny of new dietary ingredients than exists for new conventional food ingredients, and adds new safety enforcement authority for all dietary ingredients that extends beyond the FDA authority applicable to conventional food."

The root of the problem, say some critics of the Durbin bill, is the FDA's reluctance to use the regulatory framework already in place and the statutory authority it already has to do what it's supposed to have been doing since DSHEA was passed.

"Employees at the FDA and the Department of Health and Human Services readily discuss the agency's disdain for the law and their desire to treat dietary supplements more like drugs," says a former senior congressional aide, who has been following this issue closely for more than a decade. "Because FDA career staff are philosophically opposed to accepting the benefits of nutritional supplementation, they have as yet not fulfilled their obligations to fully and fairly implement the legislation that Congress passed and the President [Clinton] signed into law."

Echoing the view that DSHEA would work fine if the FDA simply implemented it correctly are the act's original sponsors, Iowa Sen. Tom Harkin and Utah Sen. Orrin Hatch. "DSHEA provides a number of consumer protections while preserving consumers' freedom of choice," says Sen. Harkin. "The act needs to be enforced, not gutted."

It's taken the FDA eight years to provide dietary supplement makers with guidelines for good manufacturing practices, the minimum requirements companies are told to meet as they test and produce supplements. This delay has been criticized on the Senate floor by none other than Durbin, suggesting that his frustration with the FDA's intransigence may be part of the genesis of S. 722.

The Ephedra Factor

Despite the FDA's feet dragging on DSHEA, the bill wasn't seriously challenged until the stimulant ephedra became a media buzzword. In fact, Durbin alluded to it, along with hormone-precursor supplements, in the press release announcing S. 722:

"Millions of Americans take dietary supplements every day without any ill effects; in fact some dietary supplements provide consumers with significant health benefits. However . . . [a] small number of products—primarily stimulants and steroids masquerading as herbal compounds—have proven lethal to consumers."

Ephedra is clearly problematic, if only because its pharmacological effects are greater, and its contraindications more numerous, than those of most supplements.

Increasing the velocity of the discussion was the untimely death, from heatstroke, of Baltimore Orioles pitcher Steve Bechler in spring training, during which time he had been taking a dietary supplement which contained ephedra.

Aside from being overweight, Bechler had a history of heart and liver problems, either of which should have dissuaded him from using the product, assuming he read the label. Teammates reported that Bechler was taking more than the recommended dose, and he was working out in weather hotter and more humid than what he was used to, all while denying himself adequate foods and fluids.

The complicated, potentially interdependent medical factors that likely set off a chain reaction inside Bechler's body illustrate how the stigma attached to ephedra has caused even the most rational people to disregard science and reach premature conclusions. Remarkably, the county medical examiner publicly attributed the player's death to ephedra even before toxicology work had been completed. When a medical examiner makes such a hasty, unsupported judgment, it encourages laypeople to blame ephedra for virtually any health problem that might arise internally, or to reach similar conclusions about others who use the supplement.

The results of an ephedra study commissioned by the FDA highlight the potentially self-fulfilling consequences of adverse-event reporting on a product once it's been labeled a problem child. The FDA asked the RAND Corp. to analyze 1,600 or so ephedra-related adverse events, and the Santa Monica, Calif.-based think tank found only two instances in which a direct cause-and-effect relationship could be established between ephedra consumption and death. If you looked hard enough, you could probably find two people allergic to peanuts who experienced similarly catastrophic reactions after eating cookies without bothering to see that nuts were labeled as ingredients.

S. 722: A Trojan Horse

Remember, if the FDA produces the science showing that ephedra is dangerous, it has the statutory authority to yank products containing it off the market. And just that threat has the marketplace doing the agency's work for it. Some companies, such as GNC, are voluntarily discontinuing the sale of all ephedra-based products. Other manufacturers and retailers have done likewise because they can't get insured for them.

What scares supplement companies is that S. 722, by targeting a product that is already being jettisoned, threatens to sink the whole ship that is the supplement industry. The reasoning of supplement opponents seems to be this: Why bother thoughtfully evaluating—and removing, if necessary—one potentially dangerous piece of cargo when you can just send a cannonball through the hull?

To understand why the negative impact of S. 722 could be seismic, consider the unique nature of the pharmaceuticals industry, whose regulatory standards supplement makers would have to meet should this bill pass. On average, researching and developing a drug and then bringing it to market costs half a billion dollars or more. A significant chunk of that sum is spent proving to the FDA that the drug is safe and effective—the two prerequisites for getting agency approval to market it. No one would venture such capital without having some chance of generating a return on investment, so drug makers get a quid pro quo of sorts in the form of patent protection.

Although the windfall from a blockbuster drug fenced off from competition for several years can be enormous, companies need vast resources to even engage in the process that generates it. In 2002, for example, Pfizer and Johnson & Johnson generated a combined $50 billion in prescription medicine sales, and their combined market capitalization exceeds $400 billion.

Pfizer's sales alone dwarf those of the entire supplement industry, which is fragmented among hundreds of small businesses and a few larger players that are nonetheless smallish companies in the hierarchy of corporate America. Two of the largest publicly traded names in supplementation, Weider Nutrition International and Twinlab, combined had just over $200 million in revenues for the trailing 12 months, and their combined market capitalization is a tad over $70 million. Under S. 722, these companies and their smaller counterparts would be subject to the same sort of regulatory codes that the Pfizers and J&Js of the world follow— without the quid pro quo. No one is going to be issued a patent on vitamin C, garlic or creatine anytime soon.

Shirting the Burden of Proof

Here's a quick overview of S. 722's implications on the supplement industry:

- Premarket approval.

Under DSHEA, dietary-supplement manufacturers (just like food manufacturers) don't need to prove their product's safety before bringing it to market, but the FDA has the right to pull any supplement that it deems unsafe. Under S. 722, this burden of proof is essentially reversed. The bill requires the establishment of an adverse-event reporting system for supplements, and once the agency receives a single such report categorized as "serious," the burden immediately shifts to the manufacturer to prove that its product is safe. This basically cuts the legs out from under DSHEA.

The event report and subsequent clinical evaluation don't necessarily have to establish cause and effect, and the event itself could have been caused by consumer misuse. Regardless, once the report is on file, the manufacturer can be made to go back after the fact and earn the FDA stamp of approval that drug companies get up front. This process could take a product like creatine, or even a souped-up protein powder, off the market indefinitely. Any new supplement containing a stimulant—including, for example, Chinese botanicals—would need what's called "premarket approval" from the FDA. That extremely expensive process is part of what contributes to the astronomical costs of bringing prescription medicines to market.

Says Seckman: "I'm not saying that this would actually happen, but what if one person had a serious adverse experience, as defined by this statute, with vitamin C? Does that mean that a manufacturer, or all manufacturers, of vitamin C has to prove the safety of it to the secretary of Health and Human Services, and then wait for his or her approval that it's a safe product? I think we all know that there are many, many studies out there that talk about the benefits and the safety of vitamin C."

- Post-market surveillance.

Currently, the FDA requires this when new drugs that have high risks associated with them come to market. Although certainly warranted in some cases, post-market surveillance is another expensive and detailed process.

Again, under S. 722, all it takes is one report of a serious adverse dietary-supplement experience, and the FDA will ask the manufacturer, no matter how small, to enter this labyrinth of red tape. What's more, the supplement company would have only 30 days to provide the surveillance plan. This window is so small that supplement companies will likely have to hire consultants and lawyers and draft a plan preemptively if they have any hope of producing it in time when called upon to do so.

- Controlled substances.

This is where it gets really scary. First, the Durbin bill seeks to amend the FD&C Act by excluding anything "chemically or pharmacologically related to testosterone," which takes products such as DHEA out of DSHEA and classifies them as prescription drugs. But rather than just impacting the prescription-drug realm, S. 722 would change the wording of the Controlled Substances Act so that these "drugs" would fall under its sway, and hence become managed by the Drug Enforcement Administration, which sets up a whole different regulatory framework. That bill would also be amended to include not only hormonal substances that promote muscle growth, but also products that are advertised or used to promote muscle growth, which could include a surprisingly broad range of supplements.

"These products will be gone," says the former congressional aide. "The fitness community will not have them unless they get them through the black market, which puts them at risk."

The Bigger Picture

This isn't a debate over, say, guns or pollution, where the object of discussion does have an intrinsic capacity for inflicting damage, and the argument usually swirls around constitutionality and personal accountability in the former case, and costs to business vs. benefits to public health in the latter. Supplements don't come without risk if you use them unwisely, particularly by not reading and following label instructions, but their basic purpose is to improve people's lives by fortifying their bodies against incomplete diets.

And, by and large, dietary supplements have succeeded admirably in fulfilling their promise. Consumer spending on supplements nearly doubled between 1994 and 2000, and sales continue to grow at above 10% annually, in large part because many supplements work so well, something consumers know firsthand and laboratories have confirmed. To suggest, as supplement critics in Congress and elsewhere sometimes do, that witless American consumers are being hoodwinked into throwing away billions of dollars on the same ineffectual products year after year not only seems condescending, but simply defies common sense.

Moreover, politicians constantly warn of the growing cost of health care in America. They argue that prevention is cost-effective long-term solution to this looming crisis. Used appropriately and in concert with other means, dietary supplements can play a significant role here. To preach prevention in one breath and in the next argue in favor of legislation, such as S. 722, that might help put many of the manufacturers of those supplements out of business seems anything but sound policymaking.

Make Your Voice Heard

Although many observers don't expect the Dietary Supplement Safety Act (S. 722) to be voted on until early 2004, Capitol Hill insiders tell MEN'S FITNESS the bill could come up for a vote in the Senate this summer, as proponents look to strike while ephedra remains in the headlines. Expect Illinois Sen. Richard Durbin, the bill's sponsor, to attach S. 722 as an amendment to the Agricultural Appropriations Bill, through which the Food and Drug Administration is funded. That bill will likely come to the Senate floor in July '03.

Congressional staffers predict that if S. 722 were put to a vote today, it would pass overwhelmingly. However, the passage of the Dietary Supplement Health and Education Act in 1994 was due in part to a huge grassroots campaign led by the industry and consumers, thousands of whom communicated their displeasure to Congress. It will likely take a similar effort to defeat S. 722.

If you feel strongly about this issue, the best way to make your voice heard is to contact the offices of your state's two senators. Visit www.senate.gov, choose your state from the pop-up menu, and phone numbers and e-mail addresses will be listed for each senator. Call, fax or e-mail your U.S. senators today. Ask them not to change DSHEA (the Dietary Supplement Health and Education Act of 1994). Tell them you don't want your access to dietary supplements (and that includes ephedra and prohormones such as melatonin and DHEA) to be limited. Ask them to oppose S. 722 or any similar proposed legislation.

Jeff O'Connell is a frequent contributor to MEN'S FITNESS. His work was cited in The Best American Sports Writing 2002 anthology.

Seller Beware: What Do Tough European Supplement Laws Say about Safety in the US?

Esther Hecht

A few months after Ed Chayet, 58, started taking chromium picolinate—a chromium salt touted for its ability to "burn" body fat—his heart started beating irregularly, sometimes pounding, sometimes even racing.

After some sleuthing, his doctor traced the problem to the dietary supplement. "It all went away when I stopped taking the chromium," Chayet recalls.

Chayet, like millions of consumers in the United States, is baffled, and sometimes endangered, by an array of dietary supplements promoted with myriad health claims, conflicting research studies, scandals that taint ethical manufacturers and general confusion about government regulations versus company self-policing.

But the American way isn't the only way.

In Europe, where dietary supplements are generally more accepted, regulations are different—and offer American consumers an informative perspective on vitamins, minerals and herbals.

Consumer safety is Europe's primary concern, and individual countries have already banned several supplements available in the United States. European countries follow the "precautionary principle," which means that when they suspect a product may cause harm, they don't wait for proof before they take action against it.

In America, the US Food and Drug Administration (FDA) must prove that products are unsafe before removing them from the shelves. "That often means that people have to be injured before the FDA can act," according to Bruce Silverglade of the Center for Science in the Public Interest, a consumer watchdog group based in Washington, DC.

For example, the FDA warned American consumers in March 2002 that supplements containing kava, promoted as a relaxant, may cause liver injury—sometimes so severe that a transplant is required, sometimes even fatal. But while the FDA didn't go so far as to recall kava products, several European countries, including Germany and France, banned the sale of kava outright. Now, the European Commission (EC)—which passes laws that govern countries in the European Union (EU) and ensures that they are implemented—is bent on getting all member nations to follow suit. And kava is just one of the many substances that concerns the EC.

"Because of the increasingly pervasive subculture in modern society, what is natural is 'good,' and every year thousands of deaths are caused by abnormal use of so-called natural products," says EC's Giuseppe Nistico in a recent report—explaining the seriousness with which Europe approaches these substances. "In the United States, the most widely used products are those based on ephedrine (Ephedra sinica), for which more than 1,200 cases of toxic effects, including 70 deaths, have been reported," Nistico says.

Consistent Continent

While US law lumps all supplements together under the Dietary Supplements Health and Education Act (DSHEA) of 1994, the EC has divided them into two groups for the purpose of regulation. It treats vitamins and minerals separately and differently from herbal remedies.

In Europe, vitamins and minerals "are considered food," says Beate Kettlitz, food policy adviser for Bureau Europeen des Unions de Consommateurs (BEUC), the Brussels-based Consumers' Organization. "It was important for us to have easy access to the products, but this also meant being much more restrictive. You can't give the same concentrations as you would under medical supervision."

The EC also aimed to provide a uniform standard of quality and safety for all member countries, since each one previously had its own laws, regulations and traditions of use. So, on June 10, 2002, the EC issued its directive on food supplements (Directive 2002/46/EC), relating specifically to vitamins and minerals. This standard enables a product approved in one country to be sold in other member countries. Londoners buying vitamin C tablets in Paris, for example, could be confident they were getting a product as safe and effective as the one they bought at home.

Vitamin Lists

Does everyone even need vitamin and mineral supplements? The EC doesn't think so. Everything in its directive follows from the basic principle that under normal circumstances a balanced diet can provide the necessary nutrients for development and health. So the directive forbids manufacturers to state or even suggest the contrary. Nor may a manufacturer state that a supplement is a substitute for a varied diet, or that it can prevent, treat or cure a disease.

But the European approach goes even further. Rather than setting only general guidelines, the directive lists exactly which vitamins and minerals may be sold in member countries, and in what form. According to Kettlitz, the list is based on scientific literature and pre-existing legislation. Substances that do not appear on the list will eventually be banned.

Manufacturers weren't pleased that some substances were left out, Kettlitz says. But they will have an opportunity to add to the list. "It can be extended following scientific evaluation [of a product]," she says. Meanwhile, chromium chloride and chromium sulfate, for example, appear on the acceptable list. Chromium picolinate, which caused Ed Chayet's irregular heartbeat, doesn't, and its sale is to be banned as of July 31, 2004, unless manufacturers can present proof that the substance is safe.

Because too much of a good thing can be harmful, the directive will soon include maximum safe daily intake levels for each vitamin and mineral.

It will also include minimum daily amounts, to ensure that food supplements contain significant amounts of vitamins and minerals. And these supplements may be sold in prepackaged form only.

Despite the directive's apparent advantages for the consumer, there are some disadvantages. It will tighten regulation in some countries but loosen it in others that previously had stricter laws. It also allows each country to decide whether it will require government notification from manufacturers when a new supplement comes on the market, Kettlitz says. England, for example, won't require such notification. Another big loophole is that the directive doesn't deal with herbal products sold as food, such as chamomile tea. "Much more work needs to be done on this," Kettlitz says.

It took 10 years for the countries' representatives to agree on the directive, which is an order to each of the EU members to pass laws that embody its contents.

But it will take some time until consumers see the full effects of the directive.

Each country will have until July 31, 2003, to pass relevant laws. Only on August 1, 2005, will the ban go into effect on products that don't appear on the list. And countries may continue selling unlisted vitamins and minerals until December 31, 2009, provided they meet certain conditions.

Herbal Perspective

The EC is even more stringent when it comes to herbal remedies because it relates to them in the same way as it does to conventional medications. It even calls them "medicine." This is partly because herbals are so widely used in Europe, says Klaus Reh of Germany's Federal Institute for Drugs and Medical Devices. In Germany, for example, doctors frequently prescribe St. John's wort for depression.

Just as in the case of vitamins and minerals, European countries vary in the degree to which they use herbals and how carefully they regulate them. Germany, Austria, Switzerland and France lean toward a stricter approach, while the Netherlands and the United Kingdom have traditionally been more lenient, says Reh, who heads his institute's Unit for Pharmaceutical Assessment of Herbal Medicinal Products and Traditional Medicinal Products. "The same products sold as medicine in Germany are sold as food supplements in the Netherlands," he says.

Germany was in the vanguard of the move toward stricter herbal regulation for all EU countries, says Reh, and the result of that effort is Directive 2001/83/EC, which has passed its first reading in the European Parliament and will probably be finalized within a year. Although the directive doesn't relate to homeopathic medicines, it does cover all herbals used in the treatment or prevention of disease or as modifiers of physiological functions, including inducing relaxation.

The creators of the directive also took into account the ways in which herbal medicines might fail to live up to their claims—or might even be dangerous. Prof. Edzard Ernst, who heads the Complementary Medicine department at the University of Exeter in England and who is considered a leading expert in his field, describes them. There may be "underdosing of [the] active ingredient, contamination, adulteration, [or] misidentification of ingredient(s)." All these can pose hazards to the user. In addition, "there could obviously be toxicity (e.g., liver damage) [and] herb-drug interactions." So, under the directive, "natural" will no longer automatically mean "good." And manufacturers won't be allowed to claim that a product is safe and effective simply because it is natural. The directive will ban, for example, products imported from the Far East that contain the plant Aristolochia because acids in this plant are carcinogenic and can damage the kidneys.

As with vitamins and minerals, the EC will develop a list of alternative herbal substances. It will include details about each substance: what it is to be used for, the strength and daily dose, how it is to be administered and possible drug interactions or adverse effects. The date tentatively set for EU countries to pass appropriate laws regarding herbal medicines is December 31, 2004.

In principle, every herbal medicine will have to pass the same tests of quality, safety and efficacy as conventional medicines in order to be authorized for sale. But there will be a simpler procedure for herbals that have been in use for many years. These would include Melissa leaf for inducing sleep and mistletoe to support heart function, Reh says.

In these cases, manufacturers will be able to demonstrate that their products are safe and effective by presenting published scientific literature—from any country—or a report by an expert in the field. And even this requirement may be waived if the manufacturer can show that the product has been used as a medicine for 30 years, at least 15 of these in the European community.

The goal is to provide a rational basis for the use of herbals. A Committee on Herbal Medicinal Products will create a monograph on each herbal product.

Careful Study

Meanwhile, work by European researchers such as Ernst in evaluating herbal medicines suggests the direction the EC will take.

In an article in the January 2002 issue of *Annals of Internal Medicine*, Ernst set out to show the benefits and risks of some commonly used herbals: ginkgo, St. John's wort, echinacea, saw palmetto and kava. Where possible, he based his assessments on systematic reviews of randomized clinical trials, cautioning readers that "because the evidence is incomplete, risk-benefit assessments are not completely reliable and much knowledge is still lacking."

Ernst concluded that ginseng is of no use in treating any condition and that it's not clear from the data whether echinacea is helpful in treating or preventing upper respiratory tract infections. He finds ginkgo of questionable value for memory loss and tinnitus, though it has some effect on dementia and intermittent claudication (lameness), he wrote.

St. John's wort is useful in treating mild to moderate depression, Ernst concluded, but there are serious concerns about its interactions with several conventional drugs. Saw palmetto has been shown to help reduce the symptoms of benign enlargement of the prostate, and kava is effective for short-term treatment of anxiety.

But Ernst hedged these conclusions with this sobering caveat: "None of these herbal medicines is free of adverse effects."

Herbal medicines containing St. John's wort, for example, can weaken the effect of other drugs, especially indivanir, which is used in the treatment of HIV, and drugs administered after organ transplants, Germany's Federal Institute for Drugs and Medical Devices warned in January 2000.

After the directive on herbal medicines passed its first reading in the European Parliament in November 2002, the UK's Independent reported that purveyors of herbal remedies and their customers were "getting jittery" over what they referred to as "draconian laws" that could "clear the shelves of health food stores." The BBC, however, reported that the amendment had the backing of the UK Consumers' Association.

Italy's Nistico summed up how he expects the EC to proceed on herbals. "It is essential, whilst acknowledging the value and therapeutic usefulness of medicinal herbs, to both step up scientific research and proceed with caution in administering them."

Information to Rely On

Despite the looser regulation of dietary supplements in the United States than in Europe, information is readily available.

"The FDA is a reliable source for the consumer. It's a federal agency subject to the Freedom of Information Act," says Larry Sasich, a pharmacist and research analyst at Public Citizen, a US consumer advocacy organization based in Washington, DC.

- The FDA Web site is a good place to start, although the site remains outdated on some topics such as ephedrine alkaloids. To find out more, log on to http://www.cfsan.fda.gov/ and find the link for dietary supplements.
- A positive outcome of the Dietary Supplement Health and Education Act of 1994 was the creation of the Office of Dietary Supplements (ODS) at the National Institutes of Health. ODS has created the International Bibliographic Information on Dietary Supplements, a database of some 700,000 published scientific articles. To access the files, go to http://ods.od.nih.gov/ and click on the Dietary Supplement Database.
- The Herbal Internet Companion: Herbs and Herbal Medicine Online, by David J. Owen (Haworth Press, 2001), is a comprehensive guide through the jungle of publications available online. For a preview, see http://www.haworthpressinc.com/.
- *The Desktop Guide to Complementary and Alternative Medicine* (Mosby, Inc., 2001), edited by Edzard Ernst and others, includes a searchable CD-ROM. For a preview, see http://www.hbuk.co.uk/ernst/.
- The EC directive on vitamins and minerals, Directive 2002/46/EC, can be found at http://www.food.gov.uk/.
- The EC directive on medicines, Directive 2001/83/EC, adopted on November 6, 2001, can be read at http://www.canarybooks.com/, under the link for Important Documents.

119

Drug Companies and AIDS in Africa
(Ethical Principles Must Be Applied to the Facts.)

Kevin O'Brien; Peter Clark

Over the last 20 years, 22 million people have died from AIDS. The United Nations predicts that without a drastic change in treatment and prevention efforts, 68 million more people will die from AIDS over the next two decades, a number equivalent to the combined populations of Florida, California and New York.

Ground zero for this pandemic is sub-Saharan Africa, where 83 percent of AIDS deaths and 71 percent of H.I.V. infections have occurred. Five thousand people die every day from the disease in Africa. Millions of children are losing one or both parents to AIDS. Elderly parents can no longer rely on their sick sons or daughters to care for them. Farmers, teachers and soldiers are dying faster than they can be replaced, further undermining essential governmental services. Because of the AIDS pandemic, economic growth and labor productivity are plummeting.

As the number of people dying and living with AIDS soars, few people have access to life-prolonging antiretroviral (A.R.V.) drug therapy. The reason for this lack of access is cost. A yearlong regime of brand-name A.R.V.'s costs a patient in the United States from $12,000 to $15,000. Even with deep discounts, the drugs remain inaccessible to most patients in the developing world. The annual budget of many sub-Saharan African families is between $300 to $400.

The ripple effects of the pandemic extend far beyond its epicenter in Africa. In today's global economy, an economic disaster in Africa can easily disrupt world markets. But the threat is not only economic. To survive, those orphaned by AIDS today often become the soldiers of tomorrow, fighting as adolescents in the variety of paramilitary groups that wreak havoc on the subcontinent. Poor, unstable nations are also fertile ground for terrorist groups. Unless a concerted effort is made to stop this present devastation in Africa and what is looming in India, China and the Russian Federation, our economic future—not to mention the delicate political balance of the world—will be placed in serious jeopardy

Faced with human suffering on such a massive scale, governments, international agencies and the private sector have committed to spend $3 billion to combat AIDS in 2002 alone. While this recent increase in funding is encouraging, it is still inadequate to stem the deadly tide of the pandemic. Kofi Annan, secretary general of the United Nations, insists that as much as $10 billion will be needed annually to effectively fight AIDS globally, with a quarter of that sum coming from the United States.

Pivotal in the fight against AIDS is access to antiretroviral medications. Until prevention and education programs are 100 percent effective, A.R.V.'s are needed to save lives, and the drug companies have them. The major American manufacturers of A.R.V.'s—Merck, Abbott, Bristol-Myers Squibb, Pfizer and Glaxo Smith Kline—have dedicated millions of dollars to the fight against AIDS in developing nations. The assistance has taken various forms: donating A.R.V.'s, reducing their price to cost, investing in medical infrastructure and education programs and voluntarily waiving patent rights so that generic, less costly versions of their drugs can be sold.

While these efforts are commendable, we may still ask whether drug companies (much less governments of wealthier nations) are doing enough to ensure access to A.R.V.'s. Most sub-Saharan African families simply cannot afford the drugs, even at discounted prices. Price reductions and other relief measures are inadequate when compared to the astronomical profit margins of drug companies. In 2001, for example, Abbott Laboratories posted $16.3 billion in sales and $2.9 billion in net earnings. Those who defend the current pricing practices of drug companies argue that profits are needed for the research and development of new drugs. They also remind critics that corporations are not charities: they exist primarily to make money.

Under this limited view of corporate practice, executives must do no more than follow the law as they try to earn maximum profits for stockholders. Their job is to respond to market forces by providing products and services that people need or want. In this way, everyone is happy, at least in theory: jobs are created, salaries are elevated, and income is generated in the economy. Any action that the corporation takes to benefit society, beyond what the law and market demand, is simply philanthropy—laudable but not required.

In recent decades, this free-market view of corporate social responsibility has been challenged, especially as corporations have become multinational. In many ways, the largest corporations resemble small governments in the influence they wield over people's lives. Moreover, advances in technology, communications and travel have made the world a much smaller place. Today, a corporation's business decisions can have far-reaching effects. For these reasons, many ethicists conclude that corporations must exercise their power in a socially responsible manner. They assert that executives have a duty beyond earning profits and following the letter of the law. While corporate managers may justifiably aim to make a profit, they do not need to make the maximum possible profit. Stockholders should settle for less-than-maximum profits, so that some earnings can be used for other ends, such as helping the community and assisting people in dire need.

This contemporary view of corporate social responsibility rests on certain ethical principles:

Principle of Human Dignity. All people, regardless of where they live or who they are or what they look like, enjoy a special dignity simply because they are members of the human race. In Catholic social teaching, the principle of human dignity rests on the conviction that each person is uniquely created in the image of God. With this dignity come certain fundamental rights, which are both political and economic. These rights are articulated not only in Catholic social teaching, but also in the United Nations' Universal Declaration of Human Rights. Among these rights is the right to an adequate standard of living, including food, housing and health care.

Principle of the Common Good. As human beings, we necessarily live in society with other people. Without a well-ordered community, we would not be able to thrive as human beings. The common good calls us beyond our own self-interest (such as earning maximum profits) and demands that we consider the needs of others and of the community as a whole. In a world drawn more closely together by communications and technology, our notion of the common good encompasses more than our local community. It embraces the entire world. Only by caring for the common good can we function as a global society.

Principle of Justice. In human relationships, we must treat one another with fairness and equity, giving to others what they are entitled to as human persons. Justice is not only a question of establishing fair procedures by which everyone has an equal opportunity to participate in economic and social institutions. Equally important, justice demands that the end result of any distribution of goods, wealth or power must respect the dignity of each person. This means that the basic material needs of people must be met. Accordingly, Catholic social teaching proclaims a special obligation to help the poor and vulnerable. It is unjust that only those in wealthy countries have access to A.R.V.'s. That someone is poor or living in a developing country is not a good reason for the inequality of access.

Admittedly, asking managers and stockholders to look to the long term and to settle for less-than-maximum profits is a hard sell in many boardrooms—especially in recent months, when stock prices have tumbled and attorneys, analysts and auditors have scrutinized every business decision. Cost-benefit analysis still rules the day. In the cold, utilitarian calculus of the bottom line, adherents of the contemporary view persist in urging managers to consider moral principles.

If "doing the right thing" as a matter of principle is not enough reason to convince skeptical managers and stockholders, then one could argue that expanding access to AIDS drugs in Africa is good business. In a world where economies are so interconnected, economic disaster in Africa will surely affect corporate profits here. By saving lives and improving quality of life now, drug companies will support markets for the future. Moreover, the companies will benefit from the favorable public relations that will come with a substantial commitment to fighting AIDS. Pharmaceutical companies in recent years have been demonized by politicians and the media for the prices of their drugs and therefore are in need of good public relations. Saving lives can create in consumers the good will that all corporations seek to cultivate. Finally, governments can encourage drug companies to expand access to A.R.V.'s by offering various incentives in the form of tax breaks or reduced regulatory control, which will lower the cost of doing business.

During the last few years, advocacy groups, stockholders and voters have pressured drug companies and governments to respond more boldly to the AIDS crisis. The United Nations, by relying on its moral authority, has effectively mobilized public opinion around the plight of those suffering from H.I.V.-AIDS. While governments must respond to voters, corporations have a unique pressure point: directors and managers are answerable to stockholders. The Interfaith Center on Corporate Responsibility—an association of 275 religious institutional investors, such as religious orders and churches—has relied on this form of advocacy by supporting its members in filing shareholders' resolutions that urge companies to make their A.R.V.'s more accessible. Recently, this has induced some drug companies to take concrete steps to ensure greater access to their life-saving A.R.V.'s.

In response to the almost incomprehensible scope of the AIDS pandemic in the developing world, people of good will are confronting their moral responsibility to help those suffering with AIDS. In the last six months, the U.S. Congress and the president promised hundreds of millions of dollars in additional funding to fight AIDS abroad this year. Regrettably, those commitments have since been reduced and delayed, and fall far below the $2.5 billion that the United Nations expects the United States to spend. In the private sector, the Bill and Melinda Gates Foundation and the Merck pharmaceutical company have each dedicated $50 million over five years for a joint program with the government of Botswana, the country with the highest rates of infection in the world. Under this program, doctors, nurses, professors and students from American universities are training health care professionals in Botswana to better detect H.I.V. and administer the essential A.R.V. therapy.

With such commitments and initiatives, ethical principles come to life. Though neatly defined in the abstract, these principles must be applied to the facts. And in business and politics, the facts are messy, the interests are varied, and the questions raised are multiple. How much profit is enough for executives to fulfill their duty to give shareholders a fair return on their investment? How much should be set aside for programs like the one in Botswana? Which method of ensuring access to A.R.V.'s is most effective: donating drugs, lowering prices or waiving enforcement of patents? What minimum level of health care infrastructure is necessary for any influx of A.R.V.'s to be effective? Of the many social needs, how much of a priority do we give to A.R.V. drugs, as opposed to other medications, and how much priority do we give to Africa, as opposed to another part of the globe?

While the answers are not easy to come by, the questions must be confronted head-on. Government leaders, relief agencies, religious groups, private foundations, medical professionals and corporate executives must present a unified front against the AIDS pandemic if lives are to be saved. Every voter and investor can join in this most worthy of battles, but there will be a cost—not in blood but in dollars. Reciting principles, such as those found in Catholic social teaching, is the easy part. Living by them is much harder, for great principles—like respect for human dignity, the common good and justice—sometimes require great sacrifice. With each day that goes by, more lives are claimed by the insidious virus, but so too, more people respond to the rallying cry to save a continent.

Kevin O'Brien, S.J., is a Jesuit scholastic and a visiting instructor of philosophy and ethics at Saint Joseph's University in Philadelphia. Before entering the Jesuits, he practiced corporate law. Peter Clark, S.J., is an associate professor of theology at Saint Joseph's University and a bioethicist for the Mercy Health System in Philadelphia.

Victory and Betrayal: The Third World Takes on the Rich Countries in the Struggle for Access to Medicines. (Patently Abusive)

Asia Russell

With the ravages of AIDs and other illness wreaking untold misery in developing countries and high drug prices preventing sick people from receiving lifesaving treatments, pressure has mounted to remove some of the monopoly protections in developing nations that keep drug prices so high.

But the pharmaceutical companies do not easily let go of their privileges, no matter the costs.

Ninety-five percent of the world's 40 million people with HIV live in developing countries, mainly in sub-Saharan African countries. Treatable illnesses like tuberculosis, malaria and AIDS kill 17,000 people daily, despite the widespread availability of medicines that prolong lives in wealthy countries.

The World Trade Organization's (WTO's) Agreement on Trade-Related Aspects of Intellectual Property Rights, known as TRIPS, requires countries to adopt and enforce 20 years of patent protection for inventions, including medicines. These patent monopolies enable drug companies to maintain astronomical prices, with potentially disastrous effects for developing countries overburdened with massive rates of HIV infection and other diseases of poverty.

U.S.-based pharmaceutical companies were lead champions of TRIPS. Their lobbyists played a central role in drafting the sweeping trade agreement. And they stand out as the chief beneficiaries of the agreement: the bulk of patents are filed by companies based in the United States and other industrialized nations.

Soaring death tolls, and three years of AIDS and healthcare activists' sustained campaigning, has drawn attention to the public health consequences of strict patent protection.

Public health advocates have pointed to the critical importance of using the TRIPS Agreement's so-called safeguards—measures designed to remedy undesirable potential outcomes from protection of intellectual property rights. An important TRIPS safeguard is "compulsory licensing," whereby a government can license the production of medicine to a third party (for example, a generic drug manufacturer) without the consent of the patent holder. Compulsory licensing breaks up a patent monopoly, and prices fall as a result. "Parallel importing," another safeguard, describes countries procuring patented medicines from a third party other than the patent holder.

Developing countries have been reluctant to employ these safeguards, largely because the U.S. government has a long history of working with the pharmaceutical industry to fight initiatives by countries like South Africa, Thailand and Brazil to prioritize low-cost generic versions of AIDS drugs and other medicines.

Asia Russell, "Victory and Betrayal: The Third World Takes on the Rich Countries in the Struggle for Access to Medicines" in *Multinational Monitor*, vol. 23, no. 16, June 2002, p. 13(6). Copyright © 2002 by Essential Information, Inc. All rights reserved. Reproduced by permission.

Through direct action and protest, AIDS activists and others forced the Clinton administration to abandon a policy of using bilateral pressure to demand countries provide patent protections in excess of that required by TRIPS [see "AIDS Drugs for Africa," *Multinational Monitor*, September 1999]. But many countries have remained fearful that efforts to undertake compulsory licensing will get them in hot water with the United States and other rich countries, at the WTO or in other fora.

In early 2001, South African AIDS activists fought a lawsuit lodged by 39 of the world's largest drug companies over their government's domestic medicines policies. People with AIDS claimed that the drug companies wanted to make profit in South Africa—where one in five adults is living with HIV disease—no matter the cost in human lives. Drug companies claimed the South African policy was unconstitutional and a violation of TRIPS. International protest-from a demonstration at the U.S. headquarters of Big Pharma to a massive rally through the streets of Johannesburg, focused worldwide attention on the lawsuit, which quickly became too politically costly for the industry to pursue. In April, a humiliated industry dropped the case.

Developing countries and AIDS activists sought to leverage the South African victory in order to demand resolution of issues relating to TRIPS and access to medicines.

The African Group—33 African countries in the WTO—insisted on a special session of the TRIPS Council in June 2001 to address the subject of WTO patent rules and medicines access, especially medicines to treat HIV disease. The TRIPS Council is the TRIPS governing body, made up of WTO member countries.

In November 2001, when the WTO held its biennial Ministerial meeting, the African group initiative would lead to the "Doha Declaration on the TRIPS Agreement and Public Health."

Public health advocates warmly embraced the Doha Declaration as resolving any doubts about developing countries legal authority to do compulsory licensing. "We agree that the TRIPS Agreement does not and should not prevent members from taking measures to protect public health," the Declaration states in one of its key passages.

But the Declaration failed to resolve one outstanding issue related to effective use of compulsory licensing in poor countries: the terms on which countries can export drugs as part of a compulsory licensing scheme. However, the Declaration promised the WTO would address the issue in 2002. Now international trade negotiators are intensely jockeying over how this issue will be resolved, with the United States advocating the most restrictive rules, but facing a determined opposition from developing countries encouraged by their success at Doha.

Anthrax and Double Standards

The isolation of the United States began at the June 2001 TRIPS Council meeting. More than 40 countries made substantive interventions arguing that patent exclusivities restrict access to affordable drugs. Zimbabwe's presentation on behalf of the

Africa Group set out the reforms and clarifications sought by the developing countries, girded by the principle that "nothing in the TRIPS Agreement should prevent Members from talking measures to protect public health" and that TRIPS must be implemented by poor countries in a manner that prioritizes fundamental public health needs, especially drug access.

Claude Burcky, deputy assistant U.S. Trade Representative for Intellectual Property, insisted that TRIPS did not pose any problem—now or in the future—to countries responding to health care crises such as HIV. He refused to concede that intellectual property protection had an impact on the price of medicines.

Burcky insisted that patent rules and access to medicines are peripheral issues in the global response to HIV and other diseases: "We believe that participants in our discussion today should keep in mind that the TRIPS Agreement—its obligations and flexibility—is, at most, one element of the equation. To deal with serious health problems, countries need to stress education and prevention as well as care and treatment if health crises are to be eliminated."

Every country except the United States had focused on matters relevant to the forum of the TRIPS Council—that is, the impact of implementing intellectual property protection on access to medicines and public health, as well as important technical disputes in the Agreement itself that impinge on access to medicines. But the U.S. negotiators resisted detailed and substantive analysis, emphasizing instead the areas in which they had no expertise, such as developing country health policies.

For seven months after the first special meeting and during subsequent TRIPS Councils addressing the topic, the Africa Group continued to elaborate language toward a Ministerial Declaration at Doha, while the United States continued to advocate vague draft language.

The ground shifted under the USTR when in October, after anthrax exposure cases grabbed headlines in the United States, Health and Human Services Secretary Tommy Thompson threatened to override Bayer's patent monopoly on ciprofloxacin (Cipro) and obtain generic versions, in order to increase domestic drug supply and to keep costs as low as possible.

In response to the threat, Bayer cut its price, and Thompson retreated from his threat—in fact, he revised his statement and refused to admit he had ever threatened Bayer in the first place. But developing country trade negotiators had heard Thompson loud and clear: the United States wished to exercise its TRIPS-compliant authority to prioritize health care when patent monopolies obstruct access to medicines. There was no more compelling example for developing countries to argue they should have the same right, free from threat of retaliation from their more wealthy, powerful trading partners.

The Cipro example also dramatized another significant flaw in the U.S. negotiating logic: developing countries had recognized that any disease-specific guidelines for interpreting TRIPS was undesirable from a public health standpoint. The United States urged that the statement on the public health implications of TRIPS be limited only to "epidemic diseases," such as HIV, tuberculosis and malaria. The anthrax scare showed the folly of limiting governments to a short list of diseases that would enable application of TRIPS safeguards—public health problems rarely operate in such scripted fashion.

But still the United States refused to concede anything before the Doha Ministerial—even backpedaling at one point and insisting that any declaration be restricted to "access to medicines" and not mention the phrase "public health."

As the Doha Ministerial neared, Zimbabwean Ambassador Boniface Chidyausiku said negotiations were "hardening" and the European Commission called the U.S. position "intransigent."

But the consensus among the developing countries was to remain strong in the face of U.S. pressure.

The United States and other industrialized countries desperately wanted to show that the WTO is not stacked against poor countries, and were eager for evidence that they "did something" at the Qatar meeting on behalf of developing countries. The poor countries leveraged this advantage until the last moment of Ministerial negotiations.

Developing Country Victory

WTO Director-General Mike Moore opened the Ministerial by calling the fray over TRIPS, public health and medicines access a "deal breaker" for the Ministerial. In the initial days of the Doha meeting, it appeared the United States would refuse any ground on the Declaration, with Japan, the European Union and Switzerland joining in an opposition bloc. The Africa Group was joined by Latin American and Asian countries, establishing their Declaration draft as the majority position.

Throughout negotiations, the EU's lead trade negotiator, Pascal Lamy, took on the role of "mediator," offering compromise proposals that appeared to take into account concerns of the developing countries as well as the United States. In fact, the EU compromises watered down the developing country demands, and were rejected by the Africa Group. Health activist organizations like Health GAP, Oxfam, Medecins Sans Frontieres, Act Up-Paris, and the Consumer Project on Technology singled out the EU as being a false ally of developing countries.

The United States, meanwhile, floated interim drafts that included everything from geographical limitations on a pro-public health interpretation of TRIPS rules (applying to sub-Saharan Africa only), to irrational disease restrictions ("epidemic" public health crises only, excluding diseases such as cancer and pneumonia) to a moratorium on WTO actions one member could take against another regarding access to pharmaceuticals.

The moratorium proposal especially rankled developing countries, who in implementing TRIPS want assurance that WTO rules be interpreted to protect public health. A moratorium implies countries would temporarily be permitted to violate rules, without establishing a lasting public health precedent in the rules themselves.

The developing countries refused these proposals, and, at the eleventh hour, the United States blinked. While not containing the exact language sought by developing countries, the final statement was a clear political victory for poor countries. The Doha Declaration on TRIPS and Public Health makes a clear statement on the fundamental issue at stake: "We affirm that the [TRIPS Agreement] can and should be interpreted and implemented in a manner supportive of WTO members' right to protect public health and, in particular, to promote access to medicines for all."

The pharmaceutical industry reacted with horror to the final version. At the negotiating round's conclusion, the International Federation of Pharmaceutical Manufacturing Associations (IFPMA) urged the United States to back out of the deal. IFPMA representatives complained that the deal undid all of their progress in getting TRIPS adopted—an exaggeration by any measure, but a clear sign of their frustration.

When the deal was finally announced, however, IFPMA and the industry put on a happy face.

Calling the Doha Declaration a "reaffirmation of the TRIPS Agreement," Alan Holmer, president of the Pharmaceutical Research and Manufacturers of America (PhRMA), reiterated the claim that patent issues are marginal to addressing poor country health needs. "We hope member countries will now focus on and address the real barriers to access to medicines in developing countries: poverty, too few trained doctors and adequately equipped facilities, high tariffs on medicines in many developing countries, the need for more developed country support, political will in developing and developed countries alike. Only progress on these issues will ultimately ensure long-term, sustainable progress toward better healthcare in the least developed and developing countries."

Health activists said the industry was merely trying to downplay the importance of the Doha Declaration, in an effort to preserve the status quo, in which developing countries did not issue compulsory licenses. With its specific and strong affirmation of countries' right to undertake compulsory licensing, they said, the Doha Declaration could breathe life into TRIPS safeguard provisions that developing countries have been afraid to rely on.

The Declaration recognizes that intellectual property protection on medicines can have negative, as well as positive, impacts on access to medicines, rather than linking intellectual property protection only to the benefit of new drug development and disregarding its potential drawbacks. It sets out the right of WTO countries to use TRIPS flexibilities to the fullest, declaring that WTO countries have the freedom to "grant compulsory licenses and the freedom to determine the grounds upon which such licenses are granted." And the Declaration instructs countries to interpret TRIPS in accordance with the objectives and principles of the agreement—important because upholding public health is a principle of TRIPS, but one which previously was neither operationalized nor emphasized.

Addressing the Export Quandary

The problem that went unresolved at Doha is how countries with little-to-no domestic capacity for manufacturing medicines or small markets can efficiently make use of the compulsory licensing.

Current TRIPS rules restrict countries producing medicines under compulsory license to manufacture "predominantly for the supply of the domestic market."

Rigidly applied, this provision would particularly undermine small and poor countries' ability to do effective compulsory licensing. Although TRIPS rules permit a country to assign a license to import a drug to a manufacturer outside the country, the licensee must have permission both to produce the drug in the country where their factory is based and permission to export from that country. Thus, even if Zambia were to issue a compulsory license for a pharmaceutical to a manufacturer in Canada, the Canadian manufacturer would be blocked from producing and exporting the drug if a brand-name company had a patent in Canada.

Since the very countries in most dire need of affordable HIV medicines are the same countries with little capacity for domestic drug manufacture, finding a way to overcome this barrier is critical to implementation of the pro-public health interpretation of TRIPS secured at Doha.

For now, the problem is not acute. Developing countries like India, which have large generic drug industries and substantial manufacturing capacity for local and export-oriented production, have until 2005 to implement 20-year patents on medicines. Thus Indian manufacturers can produce generic versions of AIDS or other drugs—not afforded patent protection in India—and export them to Zimbabwe, say, or any country issuing a compulsory license (or where the drugs are not patented).

After 2005, new products will be patented in India and other likely exporters. Indian generic makers will not be able to produce on-patent versions of these products unless they get a compulsory license in India; they will have to sell a majority of the product in India; and they will only be able to export to countries that also issue a compulsory license, or where the product is not patented.

For poor countries—and even for rich countries, in the case of certain drugs—failing to fix this irrationality in the TRIPS will undermine the flexibilities highlighted by the Doha Declaration, denying them access to medicines from low-cost suppliers.

"The problem of countries with insufficient or limited manufacturing capacity needs a long-term solution," says Cecilia Oh of the Third World Network. "The solution is to encourage, facilitate and promote the production and export of generic medicines to countries that need them, so as to have competition and bring prices down."

"Countries that are not able to produce to meet the demand should not be penalized for their lack of capacity, and their inability to use compulsory licensing effectively," says Oh, "they must be assisted. Generic producers, no matter where they are, should be allowed to produce and export to where there is a demand and a need."

At Doha, the United States implausibly argued that the production-for-export issue was not a legitimate concern. Although they did not win inclusion of a resolution, developing countries did insist on language in the Doha Declaration that both identified the situation as a problem and charged the WTO with finding an "expeditious solution" in 2002.

By late June, developing and developed countries will come before the TRIPS Council to present substantial position papers mapping out how to resolve the problem of medicines production for export to low- and no-capacity countries. The developing countries are seeking a solution that is not laden with conditions and will not require them to jump through endless hoops. They are seeking an interpretation of a TRIPS article that allows for "limited exceptions" to the rights of a patent holder. The developing countries want to use this provision to override the rights of a patent holder when a producing country needs to export to a no-capacity country.

The United States, for its part, is exploring several proposals, which are non-starters among many of the most engaged developing countries and health activists. The proposals include:

- a time-limited moratorium on WTO actions regarding production for export, or
- a change in the TRIPS provision restricting compulsory licensing for domestic markets, to permit export predominantly to non-domestic markets.

In their position paper on the issue of production of medicines for export, the USTR argues that a moratorium "would not require amendment of the TRIPS Agreement and application of the solution could be overseen by the TRIPS Council, including to insure that medicine being supplied to a member that lacks or has insufficient manufacturing capacity is not diverted into other markets, away from the people it is intended to help. It is worth considering whether such a solution would not in fact be the most expeditious and least prejudicial to the rights and obligations of members under the agreement."

Brook Baker, a law professor from Northeastern University, argues a moratorium and other restrictive proposals from the United States are an effort to undermine the gains of developing countries, post-Doha. "When a moratorium ends, the same conundrum about how to structure a workable solution will exist," says Baker. "Even worse, a moratorium, especially a short moratorium, does not give producing countries and generic manufacturers the legal security they need to pass enabling legislation or to invest in production for export . . . Clear rules are preferable to vanishing moratoriums."

Both of the U.S. proposals contain built-in restrictions that render them useless as possible solutions to a critical problem. For example: the United States is urging countries to consider restricting compulsory licensing for export to governments and non-profits, potentially excluding access among people with unmet health needs covered by the private sector. (This restriction echoes the USTR agenda in the regional forum of the Free Trade Area of the Americas, where the United States is pushing for restrictions on compulsory licensing only for public, non-commercial use.) In addition, the U.S. proposal may rule out access to medicines for diseases that are not included among "pandemics" the USTR feels warrant a public health interpretation of TRIPS rules. Finally, the United States would also like to see the process of compulsory licensing for export be as administratively burdensome as possible.

"Once again, the United States seems to have forgotten that lives—millions of lives—hang in the balance. The United States, the EU and the rest of the world made a promise at Doha, that the WTO would find an expeditious solution to the production-for-export issue left open on November 14, 2001. Now the United States [is] threatening to renege on that promise and to conditionalize the Doha Declaration to death," says Baker.

As in 2001, there is again not much common ground between the position of the developing countries and the United States on the subject of getting medicines to countries with no manufacturing capacity. Healthcare and AIDS activist groups are monitoring the situation, while lobbying delegations on both sides, demanding that they prioritize the public health needs of millions who are faced with needless death as a result of the unavailability of low cost, quality, sustainable supplies of life-extending medicines.

"To get to the right solutions, we need good faith on the part of the developed countries," says Cecelia Oh. "It is unacceptable for the developed countries to claim that they have fought for access to medicines but behind the scenes, attempt to narrow the scope of the political agreement, and whittle away the flexibilities."

Asia Russell works with Health GAP, which campaigns for access to life-sustaining medicines for people with HIV/AIDS worldwide.

Consumer Republic: Common Sense May Not Be McDonald's Ally for Long

Debra Goldman

As McDonald's awaits a New York judge's decision on whether to dismiss a lawsuit brought against the company by eight obese teens, it can take some comfort in the knowledge that the people are on its side.

In dozens of on-the-street interviews and Web polls conducted since the suit made news last month, the masses have expressed their incredulity at and contempt for the litigious kids—and parents—who won't take responsibility for a lifetime of chowing down Happy Meals. With much tongue-clucking, the vax populi bemoans yet another symptom of the decline of personal responsibility and the rise of the cult of victimhood. For the vast majority, the McDonald's suit is one of those no-brainer issues, like Michael Jackson's parenting skills.

But hey, that's how the public felt about the opportunists who sued the tobacco companies in 1994, too. And we know how that battle ended, both in the courts of law and the court of public opinion.

Lawyers for the fast-food industry must cringe every time their business is compared with tobacco. After all, there is no scientific link between Big Macs and obesity like the one between smoking and lung disease. But let us remember that it was not scientific evidence that brought down tobacco. The legal tide turned when the public-and thus the juries-became convinced that the tobacco companies were deceiving the public in general and vulnerable, impressionable children in particular. It was the marketing that was on trial, not the product.

From this point of view, fast food is in some ways more vulnerable than tobacco was. At least the cigarette companies could and did make the argument, however unsuccessfully, that they did not target children with their marketing. Fast-food companies cannot say the same, what with kid-flick promotional tie-ins, toy giveaways and on-site playgrounds. If I were a lawyer suing McDonald's for leading the wee ones down the path toward hypertension and Type 2 diabetes, I'd bring to a court a tape of the "baby's first french fry" commercial from last winter, in which a proud papa inculcates in his young one a lifelong taste for fried potatoes soaked in beef tallow.

Frivolous lawsuits are hardly McDonald's only problem these days. Its worldwide expansion has slowed. Here at home, sales are flat. Despite its efforts to refresh the menu, its customers show signs of boredom and restlessness. Those who can afford to are trading up to sandwich shops that offer "gourmet" ingredients on "artisanal breads" and other upscale baked goods (whose regular consumption may make you even fatter than burgers and cheese do, if current research proves correct-but that's a lawsuit for another day). The rest are looking for the most food for the least money, forcing price cuts and shaving profits. Such matters aren't helped by the company's admissions in court that everyone knows this stuff can make you fat.

For the time being, McDonald's lawyers are counting on the "common sense" of the court to reject plaintiff lawyer Samuel Hirsch's charge that "young individuals are not in a position to make a choice after the onslaught of advertising and promotion." Still, it is hardly unreasonable to believe that a corporation that is so ubiquitous and whose marketing budget is so enormous ought to be responsible for something. What is the purpose of all those commercials and cross-promotions and charities and supersized value meals if not to get people to eat more of the stuff? Yes, common sense may hold that, as the company's lawyers put it, "people don't go to bed thin and wake up obese." But it is just as commonsensical to conclude that marketers would not spend hundreds of millions of dollars trying to influence people unless they actually influenced them.

Likewise, it may be absurd to claim, as one plaintiff's mother did, no knowledge of the risks to one's waistline and one's health of eating fast food. But isn't it equally absurd to do everything possible to entice consumers to use your product and then blame them when you succeed? (And this industry has succeeded: The average consumer who eats fast food does so 16.4 times a month.)

Besides, if, as McDonald's lawyers argue, "every reasonable person understands" that eating burgers and fries can make you fat, how come there are rarely any chubby, let alone morbidly obese, people in fast-food ads? Is their absence a form of deception?

Which is all to say that if McDonald's and its fellow fast-food firms believe common sense will save them from the litigious and the grasping, they should think again, because common sense cuts both ways.

Think Tanks Wrap-Up
Bruce Bartlett

Gaining Weight

Dr. Robert Atkins died last week of complications from a fall on April 8. Famous for the high protein/low carbohydrate diet that he pioneered, overweight people the world over mourn his death. For many, he was their savior, giving them a workable method for controlling their weight without having to starve themselves.

Although the jury is still out on the long-term effectiveness of the Atkins Diet or its long-term health effects, there is no question that its popularity has led to a serious reassessment of standard nutritional guidelines. Even many of Dr. Atkins' critics now concede that an overemphasis on carbohydrates in the guidelines—enshrined in the so-called food pyramid—may unwittingly have encouraged an obesity epidemic.

It is just about impossible to avoid the evidence that obesity has become a serious societal health problem. The view that fast food restaurants are legally responsible for this problem and should pay damages to the obese is ridiculous, although greedy lawyers will probably keep the idea alive for many years to come in hopes of becoming rich like those who sued the tobacco industry. Hopefully, sensible judges and juries will throw these cases out as fast as they are filed.

However, the idea that there is a correlation between fast food and obesity does have a basis in fact. Economists Shin-Yi Chou, Henry Saffer and Michael Grossman found that the increase in fast food restaurants between 1972 and 1997 is related to the growth of obesity. But their paper shows that both fast food and obesity are really consequences of deep underlying trends in the economy. These include an increase in the number of working women and decline in stay-at-home moms, the increased amount of time devoted to work by both men and women, and the decline in smoking, among other things.

A paper by economists Tomas Philipson and Richard Posner looks at the growth of obesity as the inevitable result of technological change and economic growth. The cost of food has gone down, while the physical labor needed to buy food has also gone down. It used to be that most work involved manual labor—working in the fields or on assembly lines—so that workers were, in effect, paid to exercise. Now, most work involves sitting at desks in air-conditioned offices or standing behind cash registers at retail establishments. As a result, much less energy is expended earning one's living, leading inevitably to weight gain.

As time becomes more precious, people naturally spend less time on food preparation—substituting calorie-dense fast food for more healthful home-cooked meals like mom used to make. And because incomes have risen, people can afford to eat out more often. At the same time, societal pressures to stop smoking have been effective, causing many smokers to give it up. Unfortunately, as most ex-smokers can attest to, purging nicotine from their systems changed their metabolisms so as to increase their weight.

Mary Eberstadt of the Hoover Institution notes that as more women work outside the home, they have less time to supervise the activities of their children. Instead of being told to "go outside and play," as my mother always did, today's unsupervised children are more likely to be found in front of a television set or video game.

Instead of being told to eat an apple when children want a snack, they are more likely now to eat candy bars and drink high-calorie soda. The result is less exercise, more calories and greater obesity among children, who often go on to become obese adults.

Finally, some government policies have been implicated as encouraging obesity. Douglas Besharov of the American Enterprise Institute notes that food stamps, school lunches and other aid programs for the poor encourage the consumption of high-fat, high-calories meals. Dan Griswold of the Cato Institute points out that restrictions on sugar imports encourage domestic food manufacturers to use high-fructose corn syrup, which may be more fattening than old fashioned sugar.

One of the curious consequences of these trends is that the poor are now more likely to be obese than the wealthy. Indeed, obesity is now a problem in developing countries where starvation was the norm not too many years ago, according to the World Health Organization.

The poor live on low-cost but highly fattening carbohydrates, such as bread and pasta, while the rich can afford the Atkins Diet, which is based on eating costly meat, fish and other high-protein foods. The former are also more likely to engage in sedentary lifestyles, while the latter are busy burning calories at expensive gyms or on their own high-tech exercise equipment. And the rich can afford the time to eat slow food instead of fast food.

Throughout most of world history, obesity was a sign of wealth and thinness a sign of poverty. In the future, the opposite may be the case.

(Bruce Bartlett is a senior fellow with the National Center for Policy Analysis.)
The Reason Foundation
Copyright 2003 by United Press International.
News Provided by COMTEX (http://www.comtexnews.com)

Street Smarts: Just Say Yes

Norm Brodsky

Often, I've found, you do something in business for one reason and only later discover that your decision has had ramifications you never imagined. With luck, they'll be good ones. That's been my experience with drug testing, which I began doing somewhat reluctantly about six years ago.

I knew we had a problem in our warehouse at the time. We'd heard rumors about marijuana being bought and sold on our premises. We'd also seen a marked increase in petty theft and minor accidents, which I suspected was related to drug use. People were running forklift trucks into walls and dropping skids of boxes onto the floor as they were being moved from one spot to another. Items would disappear from the shipments of goods that we kept in the warehouse for customers of our trucking business. I couldn't blame all of the problems on drug use, but I felt certain that it was a contributing factor.

Still, I hesitated to start drug testing. Part of my reluctance, I suppose, was a subconscious fear of feeling hypocritical. Like other members of my generation, I'd tried marijuana in my youth, and I'd be lying if I said I didn't inhale. When the testing issue arose, I had reservations about punishing people for doing something I'd also done at their age. In addition, I knew that drug testing could result in our having to let some employees go—maybe even some good, long-term employees—at a time when the growing labor shortage was making hiring increasingly difficult. That seemed likely to cost us a substantial amount of time and money—not to mention emotional anguish—over and above the cost of the testing itself. But I eventually decided that we had to go forward anyway, mainly because of the accidents. No one had been seriously injured, but I knew our luck would run out sooner or later.

So, after consulting with some experts we'd brought in to help us, we announced our new policy. Henceforward we would test all job applicants for use of illegal drugs and hire only those whose results came back negative. As for our current employees, we wanted to give people using drugs a chance to clean themselves up. Marijuana, we explained, would show up in urine samples for at least a month after use. Other drugs passed through the body's system more quickly. Accordingly, we would wait 45 to 60 days before beginning testing. Thereafter we would test everyone in the company, including me, my wife, my daughter, the other executives—everyone.

The tests would be random and would not be announced in advance. People who tested positive for drugs other than marijuana would be terminated immediately. Those who tested positive for marijuana use only would be given a second chance. After another 45-day waiting period, we'd do a second round of tests. Employees who failed both tests would be let go.

Despite the warning, we were in for a shock. In the first few days of testing, half of the samples from current employees came back positive. You can imagine how we felt about the prospect of replacing 50% of our 130-person work force. We decided to slow down the testing, so that we'd have time to find the new people we'd need.

I had hopes for the employees who flunked the first test. Before the second round began, I asked several people if they were ready. Everybody said, "Oh, yeah, I'm clean." In the end, though, only one of them passed the second test, a young man named Bruce Howard. Although we offered the others drug treatment and a chance to reapply for a job, we got no takers. Overall, we wound up losing about 25% of our work force—fewer than we'd feared, but a significant number nonetheless.

Yet the drug testing did work. The accident rate declined, as did the incidence of petty theft. Even more gratifying was the response of the employees who remained: They thanked us. They said they felt safer. Only then did I begin to appreciate the real importance of having a drug-free company. It wasn't just about reducing our liability, or even keeping someone from getting hurt, as much as we wanted to do both. It was also about creating a better working environment for the other employees, the ones on whom we depend most heavily, the people we absolutely must figure out how to keep.

And on top of that, we got a bonus. Our drug-testing program made us more attractive to insurers, allowing us to move our policies to a better provider. Over time, moreover, a lower accident rate would translate into lower workers' comp costs. These days, more than 75% of our new hires flunk the drug test, a result I find disturbing.

Since then, we've continued to do random drug testing inside the company, in addition to testing all of our new hires. More than 75% of the latter group flunk the test, a result I find disturbing. I like to think that we're offering people an opportunity to have a better life, and it's extremely disappointing when they turn down the opportunity.

Consider the case of an intelligent, well-spoken, clean-cut young woman we wanted to hire as our executive secretary. She'd come to us through a reputable employment agency that had checked out all of her references. She had a great resume, and she impressed everyone in our company who spent time with her. I was the last person to interview her, and she impressed me, as well. In the course of our discussion, I mentioned that we drug test all new hires. She didn't bat an eye. Mainly she wanted to know the length of her lunch break. I told her it was 45 minutes. "Good," she said. "I need that time for myself."

"No problem," I said.

The next day we called the agency and said we intended to hire her. Someone from the agency called her with the news. She was thrilled. "They'll do the drug test tomorrow," the agent said.

There was a brief silence on the other end of the line. "They really do drug tests?" the job candidate asked. "That could be a problem."

"Why?" asked the agent.

"Because I won't pass," the young woman said. She explained that she was addicted to crack cocaine. She smoked it every day at lunch. That's why she needed the time for herself. The agent was stunned, and so were we when we were told why our new executive secretary wouldn't be showing up for work. "What a waste," I thought. "What an awful waste."

Understand, I'm not judging the morality of recreational drug use here. I generally believe that what people do on their own time is their own business. Nor do I mean to suggest that every marijuana smoker or cocaine user is a thief, a safety risk, or a malingerer. Some people can, in fact, function under the influence of drugs. Our would-be executive secretary had glowing references.

I know, however, that someone who smokes crack at lunch or marijuana after hours is not able to give the company her or his best efforts at work, and that's what I ask of employees. I want them to do their best while we're paying them. In return, I'll do everything I can to make sure that their jobs are secure and that they have a good work environment.

But there's another side to the drug-testing story that I didn't see until recently. The person who opened my eyes was Bruce Howard, the only employee who'd flunked the first drug test and passed the second. Since then, Bruce has advanced steadily in the company. He's now one of our top supervisors, with a whole department reporting to him. A few months ago, my wife, Elaine, and I took all eight of the supervisors out to lunch to thank them for their contributions. We handed out bonus checks and talked about the importance of their role and the difference they'd made at CitiStorage. Elaine then asked if anybody had anything to add.

Bruce stood up. He said, "I love it here, but I want to tell you I'm one of those who almost didn't make it." His first stint at the company hadn't lasted long. He'd been fired for absenteeism and poor performance. A few years later we hired him back, hoping he'd matured. Everything seemed to be going well until we started our drug-testing program and he failed the first test. "I came to a crossroads," Bruce said. "My job and my new life were important to me, but I realized I couldn't hold on to them unless I made a choice. Back then, I hung out with guys who smoked weed all the time. I knew that if I kept doing that, it would be too hard to quit. So I had to find new friends. I had to switch places I went to. I had to change all my routines. With the help of my fiancée, I did it. I changed my whole life. I became a more focused and serious person because, you know, you get rid of the distortion that comes from smoking weed. And I've never regretted making that choice. My life is better now in every way."

Never did I imagine when I started the drug-testing program that I might actually be tossing a lifeline to someone, but it sure makes me feel good to know I did.

Norm Brodsky is a veteran entrepreneur whose six businesses include a three-time Inc. 500 company. His co-author is editor-at-large Bo Burlingham.

Urine—Or You're Out: Drug Testing Is Invasive, Insulting, and Generally Irrelevant to Job Performance. Why Do So Many Companies Insist on It?

Jacob Sullum

"I ain't gonna pee-pee in no cup, unless
Nancy Reagan's gonna drink it up."
—from the 1987 song
"I Ain't Gonna Piss in No Jar," by Mojo Nixon

In 1989 the U.S. Supreme Court upheld a drug test requirement for people seeking Customs Service positions that involved carrying a gun, handling classified material, or participating in drug interdiction. Justice Antonin Scalia dissented, calling the testing program an "immolation of privacy and human dignity in symbolic opposition to drug use." Scalia noted that the Customs Service policy required people to perform "an excretory function traditionally shielded by great privacy" while a monitor stood by, listening for "the normal sounds," after which "the excretion so produced [would] be turned over to the Government for chemical analysis." He deemed this "a type of search particularly destructive of privacy and offensive to personal dignity."

Six years later, Scalia considered a case involving much the same procedure, this time imposed on randomly selected athletes at a public high school. Writing for the majority, he said "the privacy interests compromised by the process of obtaining the urine sample are in our view negligible."

Last March the Supreme Court heard a challenge to a broader testing program at another public high school, covering students involved in any sort of competitive extracurricular activity, including chess, debate, band, choir, and cooking. "If your argument is good for this case," Justice David Souter told the school district's lawyer, "then your argument is a fortiori good for testing everyone in school." Scalia, who three months later would join the majority opinion upholding the drug test policy, did not seem troubled by that suggestion. "You're dealing with minors," he noted.

That factor helps explain Scalia's apparent equanimity at the prospect of subjecting every high school student to a ritual he had thought too degrading for customs agents. But his nonchalance also reflects the establishment of drug testing as an enduring fact of American life. What was once the "immolation of privacy and human dignity" is now business as usual.

While the government has led the way, the normalization of drug testing has occurred mainly in the private sector, where there are no constitutional barriers to the practice. Today about half of all U.S. employers require applicants, workers, or both to demonstrate the purity of their bodily fluids by peeing into a cup on demand. For defenders of liberty, this situation arouses mixed feelings.

On the one hand, freedom of contract means that businesses should be allowed to set whatever conditions they like for employment. People who don't want to let Home Depot or Wal-Mart sample their urine can take their labor elsewhere. The fact that drug testing is widespread suggests either that applicants and employees do not mind it much or that it enhances profits enough to justify the extra cost of finding and keeping workers, along with the direct expense of conducting the tests.

On the other hand, the profit motive is clearly not the only factor driving the use of drug testing. Though mandates and exhortation, the government has conscripted and enlisted employers to enforce the drug laws, just as it has compelled them to enforce the immigration laws. In 1989 William Bennett, then director of the Office of National Drug Control Policy, cited drug testing by employers as an important element of the government's crackdown on recreational users. "Because anyone using drugs stands a very good chance of being discovered, with disqualification from employment as a possible consequence," he said, "many will decide that the price of using drugs is just too high." The Institute for a Drug-Free Workplace, a coalition that includes companies that supply drug testing services as well as their customers, echoes this line. "Employers and employees have a large stake and legitimate role to play in the 'war on drugs,'" the institute argues. "A high level of user accountability . . . is the key to winning the 'war on drugs.'"

Why Test?

Federal policies requiring or encouraging drug testing by private employers include transportation regulations, conditions attached to government contracts, and propaganda aimed at convincing companies that good corporate citizens need to take an interest in their workers' urine. From the government's perspective, it does not matter whether this urological fixation is good for a company's bottom line. And given the meagerness of the evidence that drug testing makes economic sense, it probably would be much less popular with employers if it were purely a business practice rather than a weapon of prohibition. If it weren't for the war on drugs, it seems likely that employers would treat marijuana and other currently illegal intoxicants the way they treat alcohol, which they view as a problem only when it interferes with work.

Civilian drug testing got a big boost in 1986, when President Reagan issued an executive order declaring that "drugs will not be tolerated in the Federal workplace." The order asserted that "the use of illegal drugs, on or off duty," undermines productivity, health, safety, public confidence, and national security. In addition to drug testing based on "reasonable suspicion" and following accidents, Reagan authorized testing applicants for government jobs and federal employees in "sensitive positions." Significantly, the order was based on the premise that "the Federal government, as the largest employer in the Nation, can and should show the way towards achieving drug-free workplaces." Two years later, Congress approved the Drug-Free Workplace Act of 1988, which demanded that all federal grant recipients and many contractors "maintain a drug-free workplace." Although the law did not explicitly require drug testing, in practice this was the surest way to demonstrate compliance.

Private employers, especially big companies with high profiles and lucrative government contracts (or hopes of getting them), soon followed the government's lead. In its surveys of large employers, the American Management Association found that the share with drug testing programs increased from 21 percent in 1987 to 81 percent in 1996. A 1988 survey by the Bureau of Labor Statistics estimated that drug testing was required by 16 percent of work sites nationwide. Four years later, according to a survey by the statistician Tyler Hartwell and his colleagues, the share had increased to nearly half. In the 1997 National Household Survey on Drug Abuse (the source of the most recent nationwide data), 49 percent of respondents said their employers required some kind of drug testing.

As many as 50 million drug tests are performed each year in this country, generating revenue in the neighborhood of $1.5 billion. That's in addition to the money earned by specialists, such as consultants and medical review officers, who provide related services. Drug testing mainly affects pot smokers, because marijuana is much more popular than other illegal drugs and has the longest detection window. Traces of marijuana can be detected in urine for three or more days after a single dose, so someone who smoked a joint on Friday night could test positive on Monday morning. Daily marijuana smokers can test positive for weeks after their last puff. Because traces linger long after the drug's effects have worn off, a positive result does not indicate intoxication or impairment. (See sidebar.)

The relevance of such test results to job performance is by no means clear. But in the late 1980s and early '90s, government propaganda and alarmist press coverage combined to persuade employers that they could no longer rely on traditional methods for distinguishing between good and bad workers. "When employers read in *Time* and *Newsweek* and *U.S. News & World Report* that there was an epidemic of drug abuse in America, they got scared like everyone else," says Lewis Maltby, president of the National Workrights Institute and a leading critic of drug testing. "They didn't want some pot-head in their company causing a catastrophe and killing someone. Drug testing was the only answer that anyone presented to them, so they took it." Because drug testing was seen as an emergency measure, its costs and benefits were never carefully evaluated. "Most firms are understandably rigorous about making major investment decisions," Maltby says, "but drug testing was treated as an exception."

My interviews with officials of companies that do drug testing—all members of the Institute for a Drug-Free Workplace—tended to confirm this assessment. They all seemed to feel that drug testing was worthwhile, but they offered little evidence to back up that impression.

Link Staffing Services, a Houston-based temp agency, has been testing applicants since the late 1980s. "In the industry that we are in," says Amy Maxwell, Link's marketing manager, "a lot of times we get people with undesirable traits, and drug testing can screen them out real quick." In addition to conducting interviews and looking at references, the company does background checks, gives applicants a variety of aptitude tests, and administers the Link Occupational Pre-employment Evaluation, a screening program that "helps identify an applicant's tendency towards characteristics such as absenteeism, theft and dishonesty, low productivity, poor attitude, hostility, and drug use or violence." Although the drug testing requirement may help impress Link's customers, it seems unlikely that urinalysis adds something useful to the information from these other screening tools. Asked if drug testing has affected accident rates or some other performance indicator, Maxwell says, "We probably don't track that, because we have other things that [applicants] have to pass."

Eastman Kodak, which makes photographic supplies and equipment, tests all applicants in the U.S. but tests employees (except for those covered by Department of Transportation regulations) only when there's cause for suspicion of drug-related impairment. Wayne Lednar, Eastman Kodak's corporate medical director, says safety was the company's main concern when it started doing drug testing in the 1980s. "Our safety performance has substantially improved in the last 10 years on a worldwide basis, not just in the United States," Lednar says. "That improvement, however, is not one [for which] the drug testing approach in the U.S. can be the major explanation. A very large worldwide corporation initiative driven by line management is really what I think has made the difference in terms of our safety performance."

David Spratt, vice president for medical services at Crown Cork & Seal, a Philadelphia-based packaging manufacturer, says that when the company started doing drug testing in the early 1990s, "there was a concern that employees who used drugs were more likely to have problems in the workplace, be either the perpetrators or the victims of more accidents or more likely to be less productive." But like Eastman Kodak, Crown Cork & Seal does not randomly test employees; once they're hired, workers can use drugs without getting into trouble, as long as they do their jobs well. "What drives our concern is work performance," Spratt says. "If there is such a thing [as] 'recreational use,' we would probably not find that out."

Asked if the company has any evidence that drug testing has been effective, Spratt says: "That's not typically the way these things start out. They typically start out with, 'We gotta do drug testing, because the guy up the street is doing drug testing, and the people who walk in and see his sign will come down and sign up with us for a job.' We're going to get the skewed . . . .They will be a different group who may be less than desirable."

Margot Brown, senior director of communications and public affairs at Motorola, which makes semiconductors, cell phones, and two-way radios, says that when the company started doing drug testing in 1983, "They were trying to control the quality of their products and the safety of their work force." Asked whether the goals were accomplished, she says: "Our productivity per employee did go up substantially . . . .Who knows if that was coincidental or not? Those were good years for Motorola."

Phantom Figures

As those remarks suggest, drug testing became broadly accepted without any firm evidence that it does what it's supposed to do: improve safety, reduce costs, and boost productivity. "Despite beliefs to the contrary," concluded a comprehensive 1994 review of the scientific literature by the National Academy of Sciences, "the preventive effects of drug-testing programs have never been adequately demonstrated." While allowing for the possibility that drug testing could make sense for a particular employer, the academy's panel of experts cautioned that little was known about the impact of drug use on work performance. "The data obtained in worker population studies," it said, "do not provide clear evidence of the deleterious effects of drugs other than alcohol on safety and other job performance indicators."

It is clear from the concessions occasionally made by supporters of drug testing that their case remains shaky. "Only limited information is available about the actual effects of illicit drug use in the workplace," admits the Drug Free America Foundation on its Web site. "We do not have reliable data on the relative cost-effectiveness of various types of interventions within specific industries, much less across industries. Indeed, only a relatively few studies have attempted true cost/benefit evaluations of actual interventions, and these studies reflect that we are in only the very early stages of learning how to apply econometrics to these evaluations."

Lacking solid data, advocates of drug testing tend to rely on weak studies and bogus numbers. The Office of National Drug Control Policy, for example, claims a 1995 study by Houston's Drug-Free Business Initiative "demonstrated that workplace drug testing reduces injuries and worker's compensation claims." Yet the study's authors noted that the "findings concerning organizational performance indicators are based on numbers of cases too small to be statistically meaningful. While they are informative and provide basis for speculation, they are not in anyway definitive or conclusive, and should be regarded as hypotheses for future research."

Sometimes the "studies" cited by promoters of drug testing do not even exist. Quest Diagnostics, a leading drug testing company, asserts on its Web site that "substance abusers" are "3.6 times more likely to be involved in on the-job accidents" and "5 times more likely to file a worker's compensation claim." As Queens College sociologist Lynn Zimmer has shown, the original source of these numbers, sometimes identified as "the Firestone Study," was a 1972 speech to Firestone Tire executives in which an advocate of employee assistance programs compared workers with "medical-behavioral problems" to other employees. He focused on alcoholism, mentioning illegal drugs only in passing, and he cited no research to support his seemingly precise figures. Another number from the Firestone speech appears on the Web site of Roche Diagnostics, which claims "substance abusers utilize their medical benefits 300 percent more often than do their non-using co-workers."

Roche also tells employers that "the federal government estimates" that "the percentage of your workforce that has a substance abuse problem" is "about 17 percent." This claim appears to be a distortion of survey data collected by the National Institute of Mental Health (NIMH). As summarized by the American Psychiatric Association, the data indicate that "nearly 17 percent of the U.S. population 18 years old and over will fulfill criteria for alcohol or drug abuse in their lifetimes." By contrast, Roche is telling employers that 17 percent of the population meets the criteria at any given time. Furthermore, the vast majority of the drug abusers identified by the NIMH were alcoholics, so the number does not bolster the case for urinalysis aimed at catching illegal drug users.

According to a study published last February in the Archives of General Psychiatry, less than 8 percent of the adult population meets the criteria for "any substance use disorder" in a given year, and 86 percent of those cases involve alcohol. The study, based on data from the National Comorbidity Survey, found that 2.4 percent of respondents had a "substance use disorder" involving a drug other than alcohol in the previous year. So Roche's figure—which is also cited by other companies that profit from drug testing, such as RapidCup and eVeriTest—appears to be off by a factor of at least two and perhaps seven, depending upon whether "substance abuse problem" is understood to include alcohol.

Drinking Problems

This ambiguity seems to be deliberate. To magnify the size of the problem facing employers, the government and the drug testing industry routinely conflate illegal drugs with alcohol. But it's clear that employers are not expected to treat drinkers the way they treat illegal drug users. Although drinking is generally not allowed on company time, few employers do random tests to enforce that policy. In 1995, according to survey data collected by Tyler Hartwell and his colleagues, less than 14 percent of work sites randomly tested employees for alcohol. And while 22 percent tested applicants for alcohol, such tests do not indicate whether someone had a drink, say, the night before. In any case, it's a rare employer who refuses to hire drinkers.

When it comes to illegal drugs, by contrast, the rule is zero tolerance: Any use, light or heavy, on duty or off, renders an applicant or worker unfit for employment. "With alcohol, the question has always been not 'Do you consume?' but 'How much?'" notes Ted Shults, chairman of the American Association of Medical Review Officers, which trains and certifies physicians who specialize in drug testing. "With the illegal drugs, it's always, 'Did you use it?'"

The double standard is especially striking because irresponsible drinking is by far the biggest drug problem affecting the workplace. "Alcohol is the most widely abused drug among working adults," the U.S. Department of Labor notes. It cites an estimate from the Substance Abuse and Mental Health Services Administration that alcohol accounts for 86 percent of the costs imposed on businesses by drug abuse.

In part, the inconsistency reflects the belief that illegal drug users are more likely than drinkers to become addicted and to be intoxicated on the job. There is no evidence to support either assumption. The vast majority of pot smokers, like the vast majority of drinkers, are occasional or moderate users. About 12 percent of the people who use marijuana in a given year, and about 3 percent of those who have ever tried it, report smoking it on 300 or more days in the previous year. A 1994 study based on data from the National Comorbidity Survey estimated that 9 percent of marijuana users have ever met the American Psychiatric Association's criteria for "substance dependence." The comparable figure for alcohol was 15 percent.

According to the testing industry, however, any use of an illegal drug inevitably leads to abuse. "Can employees who use drugs be good workers?" Roche asks in one of its promotional documents. Its answer: "Perhaps, for a while. Then, with extended use and abuse of drugs and alcohol, their performance begins to deteriorate. They lose their edge. They're late for work more often or they miss work all together. . . . Suddenly, one person's drug problem becomes everyone's problem." This equation of use with abuse is a staple of prohibitionist propaganda. "It is simply not true," says the Drug-Free America Foundation, "that a drug user or alcohol abused leaves his habit at the factory gate or the office door." The message is that a weekend pot smoker should be as big a worry as an employee who comes to work drunk everyday.

Employers respond to the distinctions drawn by the government. Under the Americans With Disabilities Act, for example, alcoholics cannot be penalized or fired without evidence that their drinking is hurting their job performance. With illegal drugs, however, any evidence of use is sufficient grounds for disciplinary action or dismissal.

A Crude Tool

A more obvious reason government policy shapes employers' practices is that many do not want to hire people who break the law. A positive urinalysis "proves someone has engaged in illegal behavior," observes drug testing consultant Michael Walsh, who headed the task force that developed the federal government's drug testing guidelines. "All companies have rules, and this is a way of screening out people who are not going to play by the rules." He concedes that "you are going to rule out some people who would have made really good employees, and you are going to let in some people who make lousy employees." Still, he says, "in a broad way, it's a fairly decent screening device."

Perhaps the strongest evidence in support of drug testing as a screening device comes from research involving postal workers conducted in the late 1980s. A study reported in *The Journal of the American Medical Association* in 1990 found that postal workers who tested positive for marijuana when they were hired were more prone to accidents, injuries, absences, disciplinary action, and turnover. The differences in these rates were relatively small, however, ranging from 55 percent to 85 percent. By contrast, previous estimates had ranged from 200 percent for accidents to 1,500 percent for sick leave. "The findings of this study suggest that many of the claims cited to justify pre-employment drug screening have been exaggerated," the researchers concluded.

Even these comparatively modest results may be misleading. The study's methodology was criticized on several grounds, including an accident measure that gave extra weight to mishaps that occurred soon after hiring. A larger study of postal workers, reported the same year in the *Journal of Applied Psychology*, confirmed the finding regarding absenteeism but found no association between a positive pre-employment drug test and accidents or injuries. On the other hand, workers who had tested positive were more likely to be fired, although their overall turnover rate was not significantly higher.

It's hard to know what to make of such findings. As the National Academy of Sciences noted, "drug use may be just one among many characteristics of a more deviant lifestyle, and associations between use and degraded performance may be due not to drug-related impairment but to general deviance or other factors." On average, people who use illegal drugs may be less risk-averse or less respectful of authority, for example, although any such tendencies could simply be artifacts of the drug laws.

In any case, pre-employment tests, the most common kind, do not catch most drug users. Since people looking for a job know they may have to undergo a drug test, and since the tests themselves are announced in advance, drug users can simply abstain until after they've passed. For light users of marijuana, the drug whose traces linger the longest, a week or two of abstinence is probably enough.

Pot smokers short on time can use a variety of methods to avoid testing positive, such as diluting their urine by drinking a lot of water, substituting someone else's urine, or adulterating their sample with masking agents. "Employers are very concerned that there's always a way to cheat on a drug test," says Bill Current, a Florida-based drug testing consultant. "The various validity testing methods that are available are always one step behind the efforts of the drug test cheaters."

Generally speaking, then, drug users applying for jobs can avoid detection without much difficulty. "The reality is that a pre-employment drug test is an intelligence test," says Walsh. The people who test positive are "either addicted to drugs, and can't stay away for two or three days, or just plain stupid. . . . Employers don't want either of those." Alternatively, applicants who fail a drug screen may be especially reckless or lazy. In short, it's not safe to draw conclusions about drug users in general from the sample identified by pre-employment tests. By the same token, however, such tests may indirectly measure characteristics of concern to employers.

The upshot of all this is something that neither supporters nor opponents of drug testing like to admit: Even if drug use itself has little or no impact on job performance—perhaps because it generally occurs outside the workplace—pre-employment testing still might help improve the quality of new hires. If so, however, it's a crude tool. As an index of undesirable traits, testing positive on a drug test could be likened to having a tattoo. Refusing to hire people with tattoos might, on balance, give a company better employees, but not because tattoos make people less productive or more prone to accidents.

How Much?

Maltby, president of the National Workrights Institute, argues that such benefits are too speculative to justify drug testing, and he believes employers are starting to realize that. "Times are tougher than they were 15 years ago," he says. "Money is tighter, and employers are scrutinizing all of their expenditures to see if they are really necessary. Initially, in the late '80s or early '90s, employers looked at drug testing and said, 'Why not?' Now employers look at drug testing like everything else and say, 'Where's the payoff?' And if nobody sees a payoff, programs get cut—or, more often, cut back."

One example is Motorola, which has seen its profits slide recently and plans to eliminate a third of its work force by the end of the year. When Motorola started doing drug testing, the company's communications director says, "The cost wasn't really a factor because we really felt like it was something we should attend to at the time." But Motorola recently scaled back its urinalysis program, which for a decade included random testing of employees; now it tests only applicants.

Motorola's decision maybe part of a trend. The share of companies reporting drug testing programs in the American Management Association's surveys of large employers dropped from a peak of 81 percent in 1996 to 67 percent last year. Some of that drop may reflect a new questionnaire the organization started using in 1997. The new survey is less focused on testing, which could have changed the mix of companies that chose to participate. But the downward trend continued after 1997.

Once drug testing became common, it acquired a certain inertia: Employers who didn't do it worried that they might be at a disadvantage in attracting qualified workers or maintaining a positive public image. Employers who did it worried that stopping would hurt their recruitment or reputations. Yet without abandoning drug testing completely, a company can save money by giving up random tests. Even if it keeps random tests, it can save money by testing less frequently—the sort of change that would not be widely noticed.

Still, one reason drug testing endures is that it does not cost very much, especially from the perspective of a large employer. Eastman Kodak, which has more than 100,000 employees worldwide, pays just $12 to $15 per test. Even considering additional expenses (such as the medical review officer's time), and even with thousands of applicants a year, the total cost is a drop in the bucket. Drug tests cost Cork Crown & Seal, Which has nearly 40,000 employees worldwide, $25 to $30 per applicant, for a total of less than $1000,000 a year. Motorola, which will have about 100,000 employees after this year's cutbacks, spent something like $1 million a year when it was doing random testing of employees—still not a significant concern to a corporation with billions of dollars in revenue (at least, not until profits took a dive).

Small companies, which have always been less inclined to do drug testing, have to pay more per test and are less able to afford it. They also have lower profiles. "If G.M. were to be on the front page of *The Wall Street Journal*, announcing that they dropped their drug testing program, I wouldn't want to own their stock," Maltby says. He recalls a conversation in which the president of a *Fortune* 500 company told him that a few million dollars a year was a small price to pay for the reassurance that drug testing gives stockholders.

The direct costs of drug testing are not the whole story; however. Wayne Sanders, CEO of the paper products giant Kimberly-Clark, has to keep shareholders in mind, but he also worries about the message that drug testing sends to employees. In 1986, when Sanders was the company's head of human resources, managers pressured him to start doing drug testing, arguing that otherwise Kimberly-Clark would get all the addicts rejected by other employers. According to *The Dallas Morning News*, Sanders, "who wasn't about to pee in a bottle," thought the notion was "utter bunk." He successfully argued that "the idea of urine testing was demeaning and completely alien in a culture based on trust and respect."

There is some evidence that the atmosphere created by drug testing can put employers at a disadvantage. A 1998 Working USA study of 63 high-tech companies found that pre-employment and random drug testing were both associated with lower productivity. The researchers, economists at LeMoyne College in Syracuse, speculated that drug testing programs may create a "negative work environment" that repels qualified applicants and damages employee morale.

The Familiarity Factor

Yet survey data suggest that most Americans have gotten used to the idea that their urine may be part of the price they pay to get or keep a job. In the National Household Survey on Drug Abuse, the share of employees who said they would be less likely to work for a business that tested applicants fell from 8 percent in 1994 to 5 percent in 1997. Random testing of employees was somewhat less popular, with 8 percent saying it would be a negative factor in 1997, compared to 14 percent in 1994. Even among current users of illegal drugs, only 22 percent said pre-employment testing would make a job less appealing in (down from 30 percent in 1994), while 29 percent said random testing would (down from 40 percent in 1994)—which suggests how ineffective testing is at identifying drug users.

For those who object to drug testing, the natural tendency is to give in and take the test, on the assumption that a few protests are not likely to change a well-established business practice. But in jobs that require a high level of training or experience, even one person's objection can make a difference. An executive with a global management consulting company says he discussed his use of psychedelics with senior management early on "because I didn't want any negative repercussions later." When the company considered starting a drug testing program, he recalls, "I said, 'I'm not going to subject myself to mandatory testing because I don't have a problem. You know I don't have a problem, so testing me is not going to fly. And I think testing a bunch of people you pay upper five figures to mid to upper six figures is silly.' . . . The idea was dropped. I like to think I had some impact on that."

A former librarian who works in sales for a publisher of reference works says he was offered an appealing job with another publisher but balked at taking a drug test, although he has not used illegal drugs in years. He told the company, "I want to take this job, but I can't take a drug test. I think it's invasive. I think it's insulting." The employer dropped the requirement, telling him he could instead sign a statement saying that he doesn't use illegal drugs. Although he ended up not taking the job, he sees the experience as evidence that applicants can have more impact than they might think. "Every single person I've talked with [about drug testing], they don't like it, but they concede," he says. "Even when they say, 'I don't have anything to hide,' they say, 'I really don't like this, but I want the job.'"

Since it sharply reduces the cost that has to be weighed against the uncertain benefits of drug testing, this willingness to go along may be the most important reason, aside from the drug laws, that the practice endures. When push comes to shove, even those who recognize the political roots of drug testing are not inclined to take a stand. A strategic marketer in her 20s who used a variety of drugs in college and still smokes pot occasionally says her attitude toward drug testing has changed. "I think maybe three years ago I would have said, 'Fuck the man. No way am I taking a drug test. I'm standing up for my principles,'" she says. "But now I have to pay my rent, and I have to figure out what's important to me in life: Do I want a really nice apartment, or do I want to hold onto my principles?"

Senior Editor Jacob cob Sullum (jsullum@reason.com) is the author of a book on the morality of drug use, forthcoming in June from Tarcher/Putnam.
Senior Editor JACOB SULLUM'S two contributions to this issue share a common figure: William Bennett, the former drug czar turned professional moralist. Bennett plays a cameo role in "Urine—or You're Out" (page 36), a deconstruction of drug testing, and costars with Noam Chomsky in "Pride and Prejudice" (page 53), a gimlet-eyed review of the two men's 9/11-themed books. Bennett also figures prominently in Sullum's forthcoming book on the morality of drug use. But Sullum insists he's not obsessed with the finger-wagging pundit. "If he would just shut up," he says, "I'd be happy to stop writing about him."

Audubon Group Advocates Deer Hunting

David Kocieniewski

New Jersey's surging deer population has eaten through so much of the state's forest that the Audubon Society is, for the first time, advocating hunting to help prevent deforestation from leading to the extinction of various species of birds.

Suburban sprawl has led to a significant increase in the size of the white-tailed deer herd, by providing shrubbery and other vegetation for deer to feed on during the once-fallow winter months. The New Jersey Department of Environmental Protection estimates that the herd now numbers 200,000, up from 150,000 less than a decade ago.

In a study released on Monday, the New Jersey Audubon Society says that grazing deer have so depleted the brush, flowers and wild shrubs that they are threatening to wipe out the population of birds including Kentucky warblers, hooded warblers and ruffed grouse.

"A dramatic change in New Jersey's native ecosystems is already well under way, and the survival and integrity of the state's natural ecosystems, native species and populations are at stake," the report said.

The study applauded various attempts to use costly fencing and deer relocation programs to manage the size of New Jersey's herd, but also urged the state to allow for increased hunting and "lethal control" programs, which involve hiring sharpshooters to kill deer.

In the 2003–4 fall and winter deer seasons, 69,456 deer were killed, according to the state's Division of Fish and Wildlife. Eric Stiles, the group's vice president for conservation, declined to say how many additional deer his organization thought should be harvested.

Officials with the state Audubon Society, which is not affiliated with the National Audubon Society, said they might also open some of the group's own lands to hunters because they are now home to deer populations that are three or four times denser than those ecosystems can sustain.

"This is an ecological disaster in the making," Mr. Stiles said. "We have to do something now, before it's too late."

While many conservation groups support hunting as a means of controlling deer populations, some wildlife advocates argued that the Audubon Society's approach was misguided. Nancy Bowman, director of the Mercer County Deer Coalition, said that the increased deer population was merely a symptom of the rampant overdevelopment in the state. A recent study by Rutgers University professors concluded that within 40 years, New Jersey may become the first state to reach "build out," a point where it exhausts its supply of developable land.

"The Audubon Society ought to be pushing for better land use laws, restricting the growth of strip malls and McMansions, reducing the use of pesticides," Ms. Bowman said. "There are a lot of things contributing to the decline of bird populations. Killing more deer isn't the answer. In fact, when you kill deer, you simply increase their birth rates because they reproduce faster than you can kill them."

Mr. Stiles said that the Audubon Society advocated stricter controls on development. But even if development in the state were to come to a halt, Mr. Stiles said, the state would still have to cope with the damage the existing deer population has caused to the undergrowth of New Jersey's forests. Deer tend to browse on wild shrubs and the buds and shoots of woody plants like white pines, cedars, hemlocks, sugar maples and ash trees, the study said. In many parts of the state, those plants have been so badly depleted that they have been replaced by other species of plants that are not hospitable to indigenous birds and other wildlife.

"Humans created the problem, we know that," Mr. Stiles said. "But it's reached a point where we have to take action."

Fact Sheet: Why Sport Hunting Is Cruel and Unnecessary

Although it was a crucial part of humans' survival 100,000 years ago, hunting is now nothing more than a violent form of recreation that the vast majority of hunters does not need for subsistence.(1) Hunting has contributed to the extinction of animal species all over the world, including the Tasmanian tiger and the great auk.(2,3)

Less than 5 percent of the U.S. population hunts, yet hunting is permitted in many wildlife refuges, national forests, state parks, and on other public lands.(4) Forty percent of hunters slaughter and maim millions of animals on public land every year, and by some estimates, poachers kill just as many animals illegally.(5,6)

Pain and Suffering

Many animals suffer prolonged, painful deaths when they are injured but not killed by hunters. A member of the Maine Bowhunters Alliance estimates that 50 percent of animals who are shot with crossbows are wounded but not killed.(7) A study of 80 radio-collared white-tailed deer found that of the 22 deer who had been shot with "traditional archery equipment," 11 were wounded but not recovered by hunters.(8) Twenty percent of foxes who have been wounded by hunters are shot again; 10 percent manage to escape, but "starvation is a likely fate" for them, according to one veterinarian.(9) A South Dakota Department of Game, Fish, and Parks biologist estimates that more than 3 million wounded ducks go "unretrieved" every year.(10) A British study of deer hunting found that 11 percent of deer who'd been killed by hunters died only after being shot two or more times and that some wounded deer suffered for more than 15 minutes before dying.(11)

Hunting disrupts migration and hibernation patterns and destroys families. For animals like wolves, who mate for life and live in close-knit family units, hunting can devastate entire communities. The stress that hunted animals suffer—caused by fear and the inescapable loud noises and other commotion that hunters create—also severely compromises their normal eating habits, making it hard for them to store the fat and energy that they need in order to survive the winter.

Blood-Thirsty and Profit-Driven

To attract more hunters (and their money), federal and state agencies implement programs—often called "wildlife management" or "conservation" programs—that are designed to boost the number of "game" species. These programs help to ensure that there are plenty of animals for hunters to kill and, consequently, plenty of revenue from the sale of hunting licenses.

Duck hunters in Louisiana persuaded the state wildlife agency to direct $100,000 a year toward "reduced predator impact," which involved trapping foxes and raccoons so that more duck eggs would hatch, giving hunters more birds to kill.(12) The Ohio Division of Wildlife teamed up with a hunter-organized society to push for clear-cutting (i.e., decimating large tracts of trees) in Wayne National Forest in order to "produce habitat needed by ruffed grouse."(13)

In Alaska, the Department of Fish and Game is trying to increase the number of moose for hunters by "controlling" the wolf and bear populations. Grizzlies and black bears have been moved hundreds of miles away from their homes; two were shot by hunters within two weeks of their relocation, and others have simply returned to their homes.(14) Wolves have been slaughtered in order to "let the moose population rebound and provide a higher harvest for local hunters."(15) In the early 1990s, a program designed to reduce the wolf population backfired when snares failed to kill victims quickly and photos of suffering wolves were seen by an outraged public.(16)

Nature Takes Care of Its Own

The delicate balance of ecosystems ensures their own survival—if they are left unaltered. Natural predators help maintain this balance by killing only the sickest and weakest individuals. Hunters, however, kill any animal whom they would like to hang over the fireplace—including large, healthy animals who are needed to keep the population strong. Elephant poaching is believed to have increased the number of tuskless animals in Africa, and in Canada, hunting has caused bighorn sheep's horn size to fall by 25 percent in the last 40 years; Nature magazine reports that "the effect on the populations' genetics is probably deeper."(17)

Even when unusual natural occurrences cause overpopulation, natural processes work to stabilize the group. Starvation and disease can be tragic, but they are nature's ways of ensuring that healthy, strong animals survive and maintain the strength level of the rest of their herd or group. Shooting an animal because he or she might starve or become sick is arbitrary and destructive.

"Sport" hunting not only jeopardizes nature's balance, it also exacerbates other problems. For example, the transfer of captive-bred deer and elk between states for the purpose of hunting is believed to have contributed to the epidemic spread of chronic wasting disease (CWD). As a result, the U.S. Department of Agriculture (USDA) has given state wildlife agencies millions of dollars to "manage" deer and elk populations.(18) The fatal neurological illness that affects these animals has been likened to mad cow disease, and while the USDA and the Centers for Disease Control and Prevention claim that CWD has no relationship to any similar diseases that affect humans or farmed animals, the slaughter of deer and elk continues.(19,20)

Another problem with hunting involves the introduction of exotic "game" animals who, if they're able to escape and thrive, pose a threat to native wildlife and established ecosystems. After a group of nonnative wild boars escaped from a private ranch and moved into the forests of Cambria County, Pa., the state of Pennsylvania drafted a bill prohibiting the importation of all exotic species of animals.(21)

Canned Cruelty

Most hunting occurs on private land, where laws that protect wildlife are often inapplicable or difficult to enforce. On private lands that are set up as for-profit hunting reserves or game ranches, hunters can pay to kill native and exotic species in "canned hunts." These animals may be native to the area, raised elsewhere and brought in, or purchased from individuals who are trafficking in unwanted or surplus animals from zoos and circuses. They are hunted and killed for the sole purpose of providing hunters with a "trophy."

Canned hunts are becoming big business—there are an estimated 1,000 game preserves in the U.S.(22) Ted Turner, who owns more land than any other landowner in the country, operates 20 ranches, where hunters pay thousands of dollars to kill bison, deer, African antelopes, and turkeys.(23)

Animals on canned-hunting ranches are often accustomed to humans and are usually unable to escape from the enclosures that they are confined to, which range in size from just a few yards to thousands of acres. Most of these ranches operate on a "no kill, no pay" policy, so it is in owners' best interests to ensure that clients get what they came for. Owners do this by offering guides who are familiar with animals' locations and habits, permitting the use of dogs, and supplying "feeding stations" that lure unsuspecting animals to food while hunters lie in wait.

Only a handful of states prohibit canned hunting, and there are no federal laws regulating the practice at this time.(24) Congress is considering an amendment to the Captive Exotic Animal Protection Act that would prohibit the transfer, transportation, or possession of exotic animals "for entertainment or the collection of a trophy."(25)

'Accidental' Victims

Hunting "accidents" destroy property and injure or kill horses, cows, dogs, cats, hikers, and other hunters. In 2006, Vice President Dick Cheney famously shot a friend while hunting quail on a canned-hunting preserve.(26) According to the International Hunter Education Association, there are dozens of deaths and hundreds of injuries attributed to hunting in the United States every year—and that number only includes incidents involving humans.(27) It is an ongoing problem, and one warden explained that "hunters seem unfamiliar with their firearms and do not have enough respect for the damage they can do."(28)

A Humane Alternative

There are 30 million deer in the U.S., and because hunting has been an ineffective method to "control" populations (one Pennsylvania hunter "manages" the population and attracts deer by clearing his 600-acre plot of wooded land and planting corn), some wildlife agencies are considering other management techniques.(29,30) Several recent studies suggest that sterilization is an effective, long-term solution to overpopulation. A method called TNR (trap, neuter, and return) has been tried on deer in Ithaca, N.Y., and an experimental birth-control vaccine is being used on female deer in Princeton, N.J.(31,32) One Georgia study of 1,500 white-tailed deer on Cumberland Island concluded that "if females are captured, marked, and counted, sterilization reduces herd size, even at relatively low annual sterilization rates."(33)

What You Can Do

Before you support a "wildlife" or "conservation" group, ask about its position on hunting. Groups such as the National Wildlife Federation, the National Audubon Society, the Sierra Club, the Izaak Walton League, the Wilderness Society, and the World Wildlife Fund are pro-sport-hunting or, at the very least, they do not oppose it.

To combat hunting in your area, post "no hunting" signs on your land, join or form an anti-hunting organization, protest organized hunts, and spread deer repellent or human hair (from barber shops) near hunting areas. Call 1-800-448-NPCA to report poachers in national parks to the National Parks and Conservation Association. Educate others about hunting. Encourage your legislators to enact or enforce wildlife-protection laws, and insist that nonhunters be equally represented on the staffs of wildlife agencies.

References

1) National Research Council, "Science and the Endangered Species Act" (Washington, D.C.: National Academy Press, 1995) 21.

2) Grant Holloway, "Cloning to Revive Extinct Species," CNN.com, 28 May 2002.

3) Canadian Museum of Nature, "Great Auk," 2003.

4) U.S. Fish and Wildlife Service, "National Survey of Fishing, Hunting, and Wildlife—Associated Recreation" (Washington, D.C.: GPO, 2001) 5.

5) U.S. Fish and Wildlife Service 80.

6) Illinois Department of Natural Resources, "Poaching Is a Serious Crime," May 2003.

7) Stephen S. Ditchkoff et al., "Wounding Rates of White-Tailed Deer With Traditional Archery Equipment," Proceedings of the Annual Conference of the Southeastern Association of Fish and Wildlife Agencies (1998).

8) D.J. Renny, "Merits and Demerits of Different Methods of Culling British Wild Mammals: A Veterinary Surgeon's Perspective," Proceedings of a Symposium on the Welfare of British Wild Mammals (London: 2002).

9) Spencer Vaa, "Reducing Wounding Losses," South Dakota Department of Game, Fish, and Parks, 2004.

10) E.L. Bradshaw and P. Bateson, "Welfare Implications of Culling Red Deer (Cervus Elaphus)," *Animal Welfare* 9 (2000): 3–24.

11) John Swinconeck, "Controlled Hunt May Be Solution to the Excess of 'Deer at Our Doorstep,'" *York County Coast Star* 27 Jun. 2002.

12) Bob Marshall, "Is Predator Program Enough?" *Times-Picayune* 2 Mar. 2003.

13) Dave Golowenski, "Grouse Numbers Go Up if Trees Come Down," *The Columbus Dispatch* 20 Feb. 2003.

14) "Hunters Shoot Two Relocated Bears," Associated Press, 9 Jun. 2003.

15) Joel Gay, "McGrath Wolf Kills Fall Short," *Anchorage Daily News* 25 Apr. 2003.

16) Joel Gay, "Governor Takes Heat From Hunters Expecting Aerial Wolf Control," *Anchorage Daily News* 8 Apr. 2003.

17) John Whitfield, "Sheep Horns Downsized by Hunters' Taste for Trophies," *Nature* 426 (2003): 595.

18) U.S. Department of Agriculture, "USDA Makes $4 Million Available to State Wildlife Agencies for Strengthening Chronic Wasting Disease Management," news release, 15 Apr. 2003.

19) U.S. Department of Agriculture, Animal and Plant Health Inspection Services, "Chronic Wasting Disease," Nov. 2002.

20) Centers for Disease Control and Prevention, Division of Media Relations, "Fatal Degenerative Neurologic Illnesses in Men Who Participated in Wild Game Feasts—Wisconsin, 2002," news release, Feb. 2003.

21) Judy Lin, "Pennsylvania Worried About Wild Boar Escape," Associated Press, 17 Mar. 2002.

22) "Reps. Farr, Shays Introduce Bill to Can Canned Hunts," U.S. Fed News 7 Oct. 2004.

23) Audrey Hudson, "Greens Cut Turner a Break; Critics Question His Stewardship of Western Land," *The Washington Times* 20 Jan. 2002.

24) National Conference of State Legislatures, "Environment, Energy, and Transportation Program: Fishing, Hunting, and Wildlife," Apr. 2003.

25) U.S. House of Representatives, H.R. 5242, Session 108, introduced 7 Oct. 2004.

26) Dana Bash, "Cheney Accidentally Shoots Fellow Hunter," CNN.com, 12 Feb. 2006.

27) International Hunter Education Association, "Hunter Incident Clearinghouse," 2006.

28) Tom Harelson, "1998 Deer Gun Season Report," Wisconsin Department of Natural Resources, 8 Dec. 1998.

29) "Deer Eating Away at Forests, Nationwide," Associated Press, 18 Jan. 2005.

30) Andrew C. Revkin, "States Seek to Restore Deer Balance," *The New York Times* 29 Dec. 2002.

31) Roger Segelken, "Surgical Sterilization Snips Away at Deer Population," *Cornell News* 19 Mar. 2003.

32) "Princeton's Deer Hunt Coming to a Premature End," Associated Press, 21 Mar. 2003.

33) James L. Boone and Richard G. Wiegert, "Modeling Deer Herd Management: Sterilization Is a Viable Option," *Ecological Modeling* 72 (1994): 175–86.

Fred Alger Suggests U.S. Cut Gasoline Consumption
by 50% Over Next 10 Years; Proposes Annual Tax
on Autos and SUVs That Don't Get a Minimum
of 30 MPG Beginning in 2008; Energy Independence
Proposal Laid Out in Letter to President Bush

"Beginning in 2008, any car or SUV that cannot meet a fuel efficiency standard of 30 miles per gallon will have to pay a tax of $1,000 per year," proposes three top executives at Fred Alger Management in a letter to President George W. Bush. The tax could generate "as much as $200 billion in revenue" in its first year, and "may increase in subsequent years," the letter says.

The money management firm says that one of the biggest issues for Americans is the soaring price of gasoline and that the prospects for lower gas prices are not likely due to increasing demand from U.S. consumers, as well as soaring demand from nations such as China and soon from India.

Alger has asked President Bush to set a national goal of cutting gasoline consumption in half over the next 10 years. This, they say, needs to be adopted quickly in order to reduce America's dependency on Middle Eastern oil, which "allows U.S. motives to be questioned, fairly or not. Reducing gasoline consumption and increasing our energy independence will enhance not only our economic and military security but also ensure that the legitimacy of our foreign policy is not undermined by our energy needs," the letter to President Bush says.

A copy of the letter follows:

President George W. Bush
The White House
1600 Pennsylvania Avenue NW
Washington, DC 20500

Dear Mr. President,

Throughout the 40 years that our firm has been managing money, the United States has risen to the challenge of leadership both at home and abroad. In your second term, we believe there is a historic opportunity for leadership in the area of energy policy, which could have a dramatic and positive effect on our economy for decades to come. Two years ago, in your State of the Union address, you underscored the importance of greater energy independence. While we support many aspects of that plan, we do not believe it directly addresses the single most important factor: gasoline consumption.

Every day, driving in the United States consumes nearly 10 million barrels of oil—which is nearly the amount we import on a daily basis. These massive imports result in a substantial trade deficit and an unhealthy reliance on energy from the Middle East.

Our nation's foreign policy is guided by principles that you have forcefully set forth. But our dependency on Middle Eastern oil allows our motives to be questioned, fairly or not. Reducing gasoline consumption and increasing our energy independence will enhance not only our economic and military security but also ensure that the legitimacy of our foreign policy is not undermined by our energy needs.

To these ends, we ask you to set a national goal of cutting gasoline consumption in half over the next 10 years. Our proposal is specific:

Beginning in 2008, any car or SUV that cannot meet a fuel efficiency standard of 30 miles per gallon will have to pay a tax of $1000 per year. For each year that the vehicle continues to be driven, the tax will go up an additional $500 a year.

It's a simple plan which will trigger dramatic change. Among the benefits:

1) There are approximately 230 million passenger cars in the United States (140 million cars, 28 million SUVs, 38 million pick-ups, and 18 million vans and minivans). Few of these meet the 30 mile-per-gallon standard. That means that in the first year of this policy, the U.S. government could collect as much as $200 billion in revenue. This amount may increase in subsequent years. Some of these funds should be shared with the states, which by virtue of their responsibility to license vehicles will have a significant role in implementing this policy. In addition, older cars (twelve years or more), which will not meet the new standard, would be exempt from the tax but would be given a ration of miles-per-year, much as was done during World War II.

2) Cutting oil imports in half will reduce the U.S. trade deficit by 15 to 20 percent.

3) The tax will spur the production of smaller, fuel-efficient cars. Currently, U.S. automakers produce about 16 million vehicles annually, but there is substantial unused production capacity. The need to replace vehicles that do not meet the higher fuel efficiency standards will lead to an increase in domestic auto production to as much as *22 million to 25 million vehicles.* That will in turn generate stronger GDP growth. In short, the sale and production of new, fuel-efficient vehicles will stimulate the entire economy.

4) The plan will benefit the environment and stimulate innovation, especially in diesel and hybrid technology. It will also encourage the development of refining capacity in the United States for diesel and for heavy forms of crude extracted from oil sands. Some of this is already being done, but not with the needed urgency, scale and scope.

5) Because there are no new untapped substantial oil fields and because of demand from China (and soon from India as well), higher oil prices look like they are here to stay. Only by increasing fuel efficiency will we as a nation decrease the amount Americans spend on gasoline. That will mean more disposable income, which can then be put to more productive use.

6) We will dramatically reduce our dependency on crude oil from the Middle East. With gasoline consumption cut in half, we will be able to supply most of our needs from oil production in the United States, Mexico and Venezuela and not depend so heavily on oil from Saudi Arabia, the Gulf emirates and Iraq. That will allow our foreign policy to be based entirely on principles, and viewed that way by the world. Freed from our reliance on oil from the Middle East, the United States could find its involvement in the politics of the region much reduced. And that would be a welcome development.

Americans like to do their bit for well-defined national goals. At various points in the past, we have risen to difficult challenges, sacrificed, and achieved the impossible. In 1941, Americans met the challenge of war and revamped production in a matter of months to become the industrial powerhouse for the Allies. After 1961, in response to John F. Kennedy's call for placing a man on the moon, the space program achieved what no one would have thought possible in less time than anyone could have imagined.

In short, we believe that the policy we are advocating will cause a sea change in American consumption of gasoline. It is a simple plan with dramatic effects, and we urge you, as the leader of this great nation, to implement it.

Sincerely,

Frederick M. Alger, III   Daniel C. Chung   Zachary Karabell
Chairman of the Board   President   Senior Vice President

CONTACT: Jeffrey Taufield
         Kekst and Company
         (212) 521-4800

AB 1058 and Auto Emissions: Legislate Now, Questions Later

Assemblyman Tim Leslie

The California Legislature has nearly completed its pell-mell rush to adopt a measure virtually guaranteed to hit most Californians hard where it hurts the most—the wallet.

AB 1058 directs the California Air Resources Board (CARB) to adopt regulations that "achieve maximum feasible reduction of greenhouse gases emitted from motor vehicles." According to the Associated Press, this is the first time that a state has proposed to curb nontoxic gases and natural byproduct of fuel combustion.

Significantly, AB 1058 does not provide specific directions for reducing carbon dioxide. It simply hands vast rule-making powers to unelected bureaucrats at CARB—decision-makers who will never have to appear before the public to explain their actions.

In anticipation of the bill's passage, CARB has already begun to consider plans for squeezing people out of their cars and into mass transit. Among likely options are a 50-cent per gallon tax on gasoline, a $3,500 surcharge on minivans, and the now infamous per-mile-traveled tax on SUVs. One way or another, the goal is to make certain automobiles become so expensive that people will "choose" not to use them.

It is alarming that the Legislature stands ready to wreak such havoc on middle America, harming everyone from small business owners to soccer moms. It's downright shameful that they are doing it in a way that passes decisions and instruments of punishment to faceless bureaucrats. Of course, this way politicians can wash their hands of the pain they've caused. Even if voters do end up figuring out who's to blame, by then most current legislators will have moved on to bigger and better things since the regulations won't be enacted for years.

What may be most disturbing of all is simply that the Legislature is taking such sweeping actions on such feeble evidence. The causes of global warming, the extent to which it is happening, and even whether or not small global temperature increases would be harmful at all are all still matters of intense scientific debate. Even more unclear is whether punishing car drivers for producing nontoxic gases will actually make life better for Californians.

These uncertainties, however, appear to be non-issues for supporters. After all, why should we wait for facts or evidence to confirm what bureaucrats already claim to know?

Certainly, blindly pursuing allegedly "pro-environment" policies is nothing new in California. Just a few years back, for example, the Legislature claimed that forcing drivers to use clean-burning MTBE oxygenated fuel would reduce smog-forming emissions by 15 percent and cut human cancer risk from exposure to airborne toxins by 30 to 40 percent. Soon after a government MTBE mandate took effect, evidence surfaced proving MTBE actually produced severe risks of groundwater contamination. By the time everyone agreed that the risks of MTBE outweighed its marginal benefits to air quality, however, the mandate had cost drivers and businesses billions. Billions more will be spent to undo the effects of the mandate.

Thankfully, AB 1058 only allows the government to dictate what a person drives. But why stop there? The primary gases targeted by AB 1058 are carbon dioxide and methane—both produced continually by human beings. Would it not make sense to establish a new "Exhale Tax," or perhaps tack a $3,500 surcharge on every new human?

Simply put, AB 1058 is poor public policy. While its benefits are uncertain at best, its heavy costs will be born by most working families. By rushing forward without examining the full economic, social, and environmental impacts of this legislation, we are setting ourselves up for yet another MTBE-like debacle.

It has been said, "Experience is that marvelous thing that enables you to recognize a mistake when you make it again." Most Californians would prefer that their Legislature use its experience instead to avoid mistakes. This can only happen, though, if our efforts to preserve the environment are guided by sound science, and full consideration is given to the effect new laws will have on ordinary Californians.

At present, the Legislature appears far too zealous for such deliberation. Most likely, AB 1058 will be sent to the Governor's desk for signing early next week. We can only hope Governor Davis' upcoming election will cause him to consider the consequences of his actions a little more carefully than the Legislature has.

El Niño's Coming! Is That So Bad?

Recent satellite observations of rainfall patterns over the eastern Indian Ocean hint that the climate phenomenon known as El Niño—typically marked by warming of the equatorial Pacific—will return later this year. Also, although this weather maker is often blamed for droughts, freak storms, and other ill effects, a broader analysis suggests that the United States garners substantial benefits during an El Niño.

Robert F. Adler, an atmospheric scientist at NASA's Goddard Space Flight Center in Greenbelt, Md., and his colleagues predict a 2002 El Niño based on a numerical index they have developed. When the short-term variation in the amount of rainfall southeast of India increases and the change occurs more frequently in the presence of strong westerly winds, the numerical value of the index goes up.

Over the past 23 years, there have been five El Niños, and Adler's analysis shows that in each case, a spike in the index precedes the onset of an El Niño by 6 to 9 months. More importantly, the index, if it had been used to predict El Niños during that period, wouldn't have generated any false alarms, he says.

The new index breached what the scientists say is a critical threshold in late January. If history holds, a full-fledged El Niño will appear between July and October, says Adler.

That's not entirely bad news. Many people associate El Niño only with damage from severe weather, says David Changnon, a climatologist at Northern Illinois University in DeKalb. Indeed, during the last El Niño—which began in 1997 and was the strongest on record—California suffered more than $1.1 billion in economic losses. Meanwhile, the unusually warm winter that year in the Midwest and along the East Coast cut demand for natural gas and heating oil by 10 percent—a generally ignored savings of about $6.7 billion.

There were other benefits from the 1997 El Niño, says the researcher. Retail sales in the United States were about $5.6 billion higher than normal because of the milder winter. It also allowed more home construction. Fewer transportation delays and less salt used on roads added more savings.

Changnon contends that the overall economic benefits in the United States from that year's El Niño exceeded losses by about $15 billion.—S.P.

Just for the Record

Some scientists suspect that the frequency and ferocity of El Niño could be down to global warming. Bernard Francou, a French glaciologist and mountaineer, is testing this theory by extracting ice cores from deep inside an Andean glacier

Few of Earth's natural phenomena have caused such widespread havoc as El Niño, the periodic warming trend in the equatorial Pacific Ocean that takes place every two to seven years, creating dramatic weather patterns all over the world. Climatologists regard it as a weather 'safety valve,' redistributing heat across the globe when localised circulation systems can no longer contain it. The normal flow of water across the Pacific—from the Americas westward towards Indonesia—is reversed and a 'warm pool' formed over several years in the west flows back towards the American coastline. Consequently, Indonesia and Australia dry out, while the American coastal deserts are buffeted by rainstorms.

Causing Havoc

The last El Niño struck in 1997–98, causing flooding, fires, drought, monsoons and cyclones worldwide—not to mention famine and disease. It is believed to have claimed 22,000 lives and to have resulted in material losses of around US$34 billion.

Nobody knows what triggers the phenomenon. But recent meteorological records suggest that it has been returning with greater frequency and intensity since the mid-1970s; every three or four years versus every two to seven. That could represent a natural shift in its evolution, or it could mean something more ominous—that the safety valve has to be released more often to compensate for human-induced global warming. Other evidence exists showing the frequency of El Niño and La Nina, the opposite, cold phase of the cycle, is marked by decadal variability. El Niño seems to be more prevalent during one or two decades, as has been the case since 1976, and La Nina in others, as occurred before that year.

Rolex Award winner Dr Bernard Francou is hoping to unlock the secrets of El Niño by coring and analysing ice samples from Andean glaciers. Since the ice has never melted, these giant cores will provide an archive of climatic change over hundreds, maybe even thousands of years. According to Francou, a 51-year-old French glaciologist and mountaineer who has been studying Andean glaciers for a decade, those glaciers promise the best record yet of El Niño's fluctuations over this time span.

To find out how much humans have influenced El Niño by pumping greenhouse gases into the atmosphere, scientists need to put together a reliable record of its historical fluctuations. They have begun to do so by studying the growth rings of ancient corals, as well as sediment from the beds of Ecuadorian lakes. The idea behind this is that cyclical changes in climate affect the chemical and isotopic composition of the water in both lakes and oceans, and therefore of the plants and animals that grow in it. The same principle applies to the precipitation that falls on the Andes—snow that never melts because of its high altitude.

"The properties of ice offer much higher resolution over much longer periods of time for this type of investigation and reconstruction," says Francou. Based in Quito, Ecuador, he has been responsible for the glacier-monitoring programme of the French Institute for Research and Development (IRD) since 1995. His latest project—for which he was chosen as an Associate Laureate of the Rolex Awards in September 2000—was to drill a 70-metre ice core from a glacier at the top of Ecuador's highest peak—Chimborazo, an extinct volcano that stands at 6,268 metres and 140 kilometres from the Gulf of Guayaquil on the Ecuadorian coast. In December 2000, he successfully completed the project.

Core Values

Francou used his Rolex Award to fund the December expedition. With an international team of 17 scientists, he extracted 400 kilograms of ice from the summit of Mount Chimborazo using a solar-powered drill specially designed for drilling ice cores in high altitudes. The ice cores, totalling 135 metres, were packed in dry ice and transported safely down the mountain to Quito, where they were air-freighted to laboratories in Grenoble, France and Bern, Switzerland for analysis.

Several ice cores have already been extracted from other Andean peaks, particularly in Bolivia, during previous expeditions—some in which Francou has also been involved. But the Chimborazo project is unique because of its proximity to the Pacific. Since Chimborazo receives precipitation on its Pacific-facing slopes during warm, wet El Niño years, and precipitation on its Atlantic-facing slopes during the cold, La Nina years, it is ideally placed to provide a reliable archive of the phenomenon.

Prior to his latest expedition, Francou, an accomplished mountaineer, had already made several successful attempts to scale Chimborazo with his team. In December 1999, in the first-ever demonstration of the feasibility of deep ice-core drilling in the Ecuadorian Andes, they successfully extracted a 16-metre test plug. Analysis of that ice has shown that its composition tells the same story as meteorological records for the last several years, which means the technique is reliable.

Claude Lorius, director of the French Polar Institute and a specialist in the field, says, "The information that this drilling could provide is of the greatest importance. By understanding El Niño evolution over a long stretch of time, we will be able to improve our understanding of the mechanisms that cause these events."

Francou himself contends, "The success of this project will have great repercussions at an international level. If it were possible to accurately predict El Niño events, as it may be in the near future, the lives of those inhabiting the entire tropics—half of the world's population—could be improved immeasurably."

For further information about the December 2000 expedition go to www.inamhi.gov.ec/Chimborazo2000

172